PROPHET OF PROGRESS

BY T. A. BOYD

PROFESSIONAL AMATEUR: The Biography of Charles Franklin Kettering. PROPHET OF PROGRESS: Selections from the Speeches of Charles F. Kettering

Charles F. Kettering at age 80

Edited by T. A. Boyd

PROPHET OF PROGRESS

SELECTIONS FROM THE SPEECHES OF

CHARLES F. KETTERING

E. P. DUTTON AND CO., INC.
NEW YORK

To my Daughter
ELINOR JEAN BOYD
One of the multitude of
Young People, present and future,
for whom there is special significance in
the progressive sayings of
CHARLES F. KETTERING

"NOTHING EVER BUILT AROSE TO TOUCH THE SKIES
UNLESS SOME MAN DREAMED THAT IT SHOULD, SOME MAN
BELIEVED THAT IT COULD, AND SOME MAN WILLED THAT
IT MUST."   —CHARLES F. KETTERING

CONTENTS

APPENDIX

INTRODUCTION

DURING HIS CAREER CHARLES F. KETTERING MADE HUNDREDS of speeches. The audiences he addressed were of many kinds —businessmen, educators, farmers, engineers, scientists, young people, listeners of every sort.

He spoke out of an imaginative mind and a wide experience in life. Farm boy, country schoolteacher, and Friday night debater, he became an eminent engineer, scientist, inventor, philosopher, educator, and pioneer of industry. Through it all, he was a dedicated and eloquent prophet of progress. Young people and women liked to hear Kettering speak, because his addresses were so warmhearted and inspirational.

A distinctive feature of Kettering's speeches was that nearly all of them were impromptu. Except for some radio talks, none was prepared in advance. In the selections contained in this volume an effort has been made to retain the spontaneity and informality of the originals, for such free-spirited word painting was his accustomed manner of speaking.

To add clarity and emphasis to his utterances, Kettering made liberal use of exaggeration and oversimplification, and his sayings need to be read with an understanding of that circumstance.

Each of two of the chapters in this volume (V and VI) is based on a single address. But the others are composites of utterances selected from a number of Kettering's speeches—speeches which he made over a period of more than forty years.

Incorporated in the material in this volume are a few short extracts from published interviews with Kettering and from articles by him. For these acknowledgment is made to *The Saturday Evening Post, The Rotarian, School and Society, Nation's Business,* and some others of the periodicals in the List of Publications in the Appendix.

T. A. Boyd

PROPHET OF PROGRESS

OPPORTUNITIES UNLIMITED

Kettering's thought and much of what he said related to the future. At a luncheon in his honor on the twenty-fifth anniversary of his development of the electric self-starter he said, "I have no desire to meditate or philosophize upon the past. I have only one wish, and that is to direct our eyes toward the infinite future."

I DON'T LIKE TO SEE PEOPLE PAINTING THE FUTURE WITH A black brush. I expect to spend all the rest of my life there, and I would like it to be a nice place, polished, bright, glistening, and glorious.

No matter how black you paint the future—and there are some very good painters, too—it is a beautiful picture compared to the road you have come over. I am not a Pollyanna optimist in any sense, and I do not believe the world is a goody-goody place or anything like that. I am not optimistic in the sense of believing that there is no trouble ahead.

But I do believe you can make human progress and scientific progress and get much better living conditions, better health, and better this and better that when you are willing to pay the price. As I have often said, the price of progress is trouble. It is made up of long hours of hard work, disappointments, criticism, and often physical as well as mental discomforts. If you do not want to pay that price for human progress, then you pay a much greater price for standing still.

There are a lot of new things ahead of us and that is when life is really interesting—when you know something is ahead. Even a body of soldiers standing marking time, if they can just walk a little forward they are happier. If you keep them standing in one spot they get "sore," but if they can just move forward a little they are all right.

The reason that I have hope for the future is that we don't know very much yet. We think we are further along the path of knowledge than we actually are. We're so busy clapping ourselves on the back for what we've done up to now that we forget we're submerged in infinite ignorance. A man once expressed the imperfect state of our knowledge in what I think was the nicest way I ever heard. He said, "We are reading the first verses in the first chapter of a book whose pages are infinite."

Suppose we had a big letter file here in front of us with just one letter written each year during the period in which man has been able to write—one of those state-of-the-nation type of letters. You could pull out any letter and it would read just the same as the others. It is a universal letter, and it would say: "We don't see how the people who lived before us got along with what they had to do with, but we can't see much chance for improvement in the future."

The accomplishments thus far seem so amazing to us that it is difficult to visualize the continuance of important developments in the future. But we are still in the kindergarten and should not let our present accomplishments prevent us from seeing how little we really do know and what great opportunities there are for advancement. Personally, I believe that the future is an immense storehouse of inventions and discoveries just waiting for someone to come along and unlock the door.

I have said I was pretty sure that man came from the crab family because we back into everything. We don't go straight forward at all. I think it is time we turned around and faced the future with our backs to history. You can't have a better tomorrow if you are thinking about yesterday all the time. If you want to back into history far enough to get some bearings, that is perfectly all right. But keep looking forward, because your life is going to be spent in the future. I wouldn't discount the past or overemphasize the future. Let us remember, though, that we don't so much care where we came from, but that we'd like to know where we are going.

We can be residents in space. We can live any place we want to, but we're going to be transients in time. Tomorrow's going to be another day. Now that's what causes all the trouble. We're all the time talking about "the good old days," because then is when we thought we had arrived. So we sometimes pull down the curtains on our thinking, and that is a most dangerous thing for an organization or an individual to do. You can't expect to arrive at any position where you have a fixed thing, because as long as you breathe, as long as the plants grow, there is no terminal point. You live in an atmosphere of perpetual change.

So you can't avoid the future. What are you going to do with it then? I say that it should be compulsory on our part to use it in the best way we can. The greatest thing this generation can do is to lay a few steppingstones for the next generation.

Thomas Midgley, Jr., was one of my most productive associates in research. Midgley was a man who had those vital characteristics of a successful research man, versatility and action, and he was like a son or brother to me. But he died at the age of fifty-five, and at his funeral the minister read the familiar Bible verse, "We brought nothing into this world, and it is certain we can carry nothing out." Knowing the highly creative life Midgley had lived, it struck me then that in his case it would have seemed appropriate to have added this: "But we can leave a lot behind for the good of the world."

We have to learn how to look forward. Some people like to plan too exactly, and you can't plan exactly. You have to plan with a broad scope. You have seen these systematic types of persons who say, "We've got that fixed. Let's fasten it down." I call such people "hot riveters." As soon as they get a situation set up, they want to rivet it—make it permanent, so to speak. After a while they are busy cutting loose things they don't have right. If you get enough of those, it takes all your time to undo what you have that isn't right. I like to plan for tomorrow and make another plan for the next day and keep building up. You ought to do a little bit better tomorrow because you have had a day's experience.

But you never get anything set to a pattern. If things worked the way they look as though they should you could write the history of the world in advance. They won't often work out the way philosophy says they ought. Sometimes, however, it is those deviations from the normal, as we think of it, that make for human progress.

But we can do a little something about the future. We can try to plan intelligently, and by that I mean we can try to plan ourselves out of the established grooves into which we have sunk. Grooves are comfortable things, because they follow beaten tracks. The only way to progress is to cut across the grooves and that is always a bumpy proposition.

Often I have told this story about beaten tracks. My home is in Dayton. But I can't get a job there. So I work in Detroit and I have driven back and forth for years. It is about 220 miles. A friend of mine who makes the trip once in a while said to me, "I understand you make that trip in four hours and a half."

"Yes, I do," I said.

"Well," he replied, "I'm a better driver than you, and I can't do it in that time."

So I asked him to go along with me one day. When we made the trip in just four hours and a half, he said, "No wonder you can do it in that time. You don't stay on Route 25!" [1]

In my opinion, we have to date chipped away only a few fragments from the Mountain of Knowledge—fragments that have changed our entire way of life. But looming ahead of us, practically intact, lies a huge mass of fundamental facts any one of which, if uncovered, could change our civilization.

In that mountain lies the solution to the problem of how we can utilize the practically limitless energy of the sun pouring down on the earth, and there also is the answer to the age-old problem of feeding the millions of undernourished people in the world. Somewhere in that mass are the cures for cancer, the common cold, and other ills that beset the human race. Just out of reach there, today, is the design for a successful interplanetary space ship. And I am sure someone, on the most important date in the history of mankind, will find the answer to world peace.

---

[1] This was said before the new U.S. 25 through Ohio, which by-passes many towns and cities, was constructed.

The world is not finished and put up in a box. I can conceive of nothing more foolish than for us to say the world is finished. If we keep our minds on the job, have faith in ourselves and others, there is nothing we can dream about that we can't have. I think anybody can write the most fantastic thing about the future of this country of ours and it will be too little in the end.

No, I am not being too visionary. On the contrary, I know that by the wildest stretch of the imagination none of us here today could even begin to paint a true picture of the future. History has shown that it has always surpassed man's feeble attempts at prophecy. Remember Jules Verne, H. G. Wells, and the others who wrote predictions of the future. They missed it by miles. What is equally important, they missed it in a way that they thought it wouldn't be possible to miss. You can write your ticket for the future, and when you do you will be sure to under-write it, for the imagination of the best of us comes far short of the actualities as they develop.

So I want to resell your faith in the future, faith in America, faith in human nature. You've got to work and continue to strive for what you hope to attain, and be patient. Human progress is not a physical thing, but a mental thing. And it will go on just as long as we keep our eyes up and our vision clear enough to see what is yet to be accomplished and what new services can be given to the human family.

I have lost patience with people who go around with tears in their eyes, weeping and wailing about there being no opportunities for the young fellow today. I hate for the world to go ahead living in this atmosphere of fear. Some people begin to get fearful much faster than they get intelligent, it seems. They may possibly have been listening to some radio commentators and newspaper columnists who cannot hold their jobs unless they scare you. The columnist has a wife and family to support. He has to make us read his column by sprinkling it with just enough concern so that we do read it.

Not too long ago I suggested to the broadcasting people that we have one hour on our great radio systems called the "Happiness

Hour." That they have a news commentator or somebody like that who would tell what a perfectly wonderful country we have here today, and that it isn't going where they think it is going at all. It is going in exactly the opposite direction.[2]

Man will continue to be the changeful, lively, impulsive creature he has always been, the kind of fellow who won't do what you want him to do if he doesn't want to do it, and who will do twenty times the work you think he can do if he takes the notion and is actuated by adequate and proper motivation. He will still be the kind of chap who, after proving that he can build one kind of house or building, is no longer interested in building that kind any more, but in going on and building something different.

Never were there such opportunities for young men and young women of ability as there are today. It is perfectly true that there are not the same opportunities for the same things as there were fifty years ago. I think opportunity does not exist in this country but in the *minds* of the people. We must open up a new field, and there are thousands of new fields standing waiting. For we are not at the end of our progress but at the beginning. We have but reached the shores of a great unexplored continent. We cannot turn back. It is man's destiny to ponder on the riddle of existence and, as a by-product of his wonderment, to create a new life on this earth.

When we look at an acorn it is sometimes difficult to imagine the giant oak. By the same token there are probably young people around us, in every community, whose ideas and work will set the pattern for our civilization fifty years hence. We must be careful then not to overemphasize today's problems to the extent that we neglect the long-range view and fail to encourage these thinkers and builders of the world of tomorrow.

As we turn a young person's attention to things undone or done badly, the riddles of waste and want yet to be solved, the discoveries yet to be made, the symphonies yet to be written, we must make him feel that in the world of tomorrow there'll be plenty of opportunity for *him* to do these things, or other things which are just as

---

[2] Said in 1950 at a Junior Achievement dinner.

important. But it must be emphasized that the right to exercise his highest faculties in changing the world must be won by a thorough and driving preparation.

I wish I could say, in language so dramatic that it would impress you deeply, what I think our opportunities are. The best words I can find for doing so are these: *This is the golden age of opportunity, the age of opportunity unlimited!*

EDUCATION FOR TOMORROW

A keen interest in education and a lifelong effort to assist it were natural to Kettering. Himself a schoolteacher in early life, he gave education his counsel and criticism; his aid, material and personal; and his eloquent support. Many of his speeches were made to educators and to high school and college students.

I HAVE BEEN IN EDUCATION ALL MY LIFE. I STARTED OUT AS A schoolteacher and have been associated with educational institutions ever since. My definition of an educated man is the fellow who knows the right thing to do at the time it has to be done. You can be sincere and still be stupid.

There is a great difference between knowing a thing and understanding it. You can know a lot and not really understand anything.

So much of our information today does not consist of basic understanding. It is known to us only by definitions. We say a copper wire is a conductor of electricity. But our best scientists do not know, even in a small way, how electricity passes through a wire. The trouble is that we don't get interested in the commonplace things. And it is the commonplace things that go to make up the universe.

We often think that by naming something we know all about it, and the more complicated the name the more we know. I was talking to a good friend of mine, Dr. Martin Fischer, who is professor of physiology at the University of Cincinnati and is also one of the cleverest speakers in the country. "You know," he said, "I gave a lecture to my students some time ago about how important it is to be smart. I used an illustration about an old fellow who came to me, pulled up the leg of his pants and asked me what some big red spots were. I gave him a name for them in Greek. 'Gosh, Doc,' he said, 'you know everything.'"

Actually, we know practically nothing. I believe that the motto which should be adopted by every thinking person is: We are igno-

23

rant insofar as we think we are wise, and we are wise insofar as we know we are ignorant. Argument is always an indication of lack of knowledge. And when two fellows argue, either one of them is right and the other is wrong, or they are both part right and part wrong, or both of them are wrong—and it is usually the latter.

If I should ask you how long this table is, and each of you were to write down how long you think it is, we could sit around and argue about it. We could continue to argue just as much as we wanted to. The table wouldn't change its length whatever our opinions. But the foolish fellow who continues to argue after we have *measured* the table gets thrown out of the room.

In reality, as I have said before, we have only begun to knock a few chips from the great quarry of knowledge that has been given us to dig out and use. We are like the two fellows who started to walk from New York to San Francisco. When they got over into New Jersey, one said: "We must be pretty nearly there. We have been walking a long, long time." That is just how we are in what we know technically. We have just barely begun.

The schools should therefore teach us that we know very little about anything. Our educators should simply say to the student that this is the best package we can give you today and that some is going to fall out tomorrow and some is going to stay longer and some will be in there when the world is finished. Somebody is doing something right now, some place in the world, that is changing a fact we had yesterday into a questionable thing today.

I have a boy about fourteen years old who has a radio outfit.[1] He asked me in which direction the current from a storage battery goes. I told him that until very recently everyone supposed that the current flowed from the positive terminal to the negative, but it has now been definitely proved that just the opposite is the case. Benjamin Franklin took a piece of silk and a cat's skin. He stroked the cat fur and called the electricity produced positive. He did the same with the silk and called that electricity negative. This was purely

[1] Said in 1923.

accident. But we accepted it for many years until it was found that electricity flows not from the positive to the negative but from the negative to the positive.

We need to recognize that we are educating these young people to live in tomorrow, not in the past. And it is so much easier to teach where we came from than it is to open up the door to where we are going. Some good inventor should invent the opposite word for history, a word which would mean looking forward in the same way that history means looking backward. "Hysterics" has been suggested, but I don't think that is a good word. It applies more to history in the making than to the future.

If we drove an automobile the way we try to run civilization, I think we would face backward, looking through the back window, admiring where we came from, and not caring where we are going. If you want a good life, you must look to the future. I think it is all right to have courses in history, but history is the "gonest" thing in the world. Let's keep history, but let's take a small part of the time and study where we are going. *That* is the important thing. We can do something about the unmade history. But we must look where we are going and not where we've been. We must use the past as a guidepost, not as a hitching post.

There are two ways in which people look at the future: one, it is going to be a great new world, unlike anything else that has ever happened; and the other, it is going to be a very dark place. It seems to me that that method of thinking is a good bit like the electric light switch. It has to be either on or off. I think there are a lot of intermediate points between full on and full off, and we can have a world that doesn't have to be a bright new glowing world, or a world that goes to the dark places where a world goes when it is finished. So, I think we need to look at this world as a reality.

I have such great confidence in the young men and women of today's vintage that I will bet my right eye on them, because I think if we will stop telling them that there is no hope, there is no chance, and tell them instead, "There is a job; go and get it done," they will accomplish something.

A prominent physicist once told me that I could never understand space physics because I was a materialist. You have to have something to make a model of in your mind, he said. And I accept that. I am a materialist. I have still got to make my engines out of pieces.

You can't understand the radio wave and radiation is beyond you, said the physicist. If you are a good scientist you can think of that without visualizing any material thing. We can prove that you can't visualize space, because there is nothing in space. You can't mechanize space. So your philosophy of physics is all wrong.

But I have tried this elementary experiment, and all I asked him for was an explanation of the experiment, which was this: While in London one time I went down to see Big Ben, because I happened to be with a fellow working for the National Broadcasting Company and he was going to make some changes on the microphone there.

A part of Big Ben is, of course, a great big bell and a big hammer, certainly mechanical in every sense of the word. You don't have any trouble visualizing that at all. And back there in a protected place, so it doesn't get the rain and the wind, is a microphone. That too is mechanical, because you can take it apart and see it.

Now, you go along with me all right until that sound gets out on the antenna, I said to him. There is where you have got to leave off. That is space, you say. And that is all right.

Now, at the time Big Ben was striking the hour which was broadcast I had a phonograph record made. It was made by the old-fashioned mechanical means. It was not an electrical transcription. I bring that record over here and put it on a good electrical reproducing phonograph and it sounds just like Big Ben.

At the same time I sit alongside a radio set. I tune it in, and when that clock strikes over there in London you hear a sound which is just like Big Ben. Well, it is Big Ben. That sound went in mechanical and it comes out mechanical. If you put your finger on the diaphragm of the receiver, you can feel the hammer hit the bell.

If the first time it had sounded like a canary bird and the second like a cuckoo, then I would agree that you had something. But the sound is exactly like that which started at the other end. If this isn't mechanical, it is very definitely related, I said. But in actuality our knowledge about the mode of transmission ends at the foot of the antenna. So why don't we, both of us, just say that this is something we don't know anything about?

The thing we need to recognize today is that the fundamental of education is to take the material that the Lord gave us and make the most of it. If a boy is left-handed, let him be left-handed, but make him the best left-handed person you ever saw.

I used to be a teacher in a country school, and there I had as a first year pupil a little girl who could read already, provided she held the book upside down. I wondered why that was. So I went to her home and here was the story—simple as could be. She had an invalid grandmother, and the girl sat on a stool in front of the grandmother as she read to her. In that way the child had learned to read herself. The question of right side up and upside down depends on which way you start to hold the book.

But you can't go through life reading newspapers upside down. So I got a music rack, turned the book a few degrees each week, and so got the little girl to reading right side up.

If I were writing the engineering course, I would write only three things—four years of physics, four years of chemistry, and three years of mathematics, and then you might fill in with anything else you want, including a little history and economics. The "how" and "why" of fundamentals should be inculcated to form the foundation for the approach to any problem. With that foundation I can take a man and teach him about a gas engine if he has never seen one. But I cannot take a specialist, if he has not had a basic education, because I cannot get it over to him if I work until doomsday.

I don't think it makes much difference what course you take in college, provided you get a broad concept and learn how to attack problems. I want to sound a note of warning against too high a degree of specialization, especially in the field of engineering.

Thomas Midgley, Jr., who developed tetraethyl lead as an anti-knock agent for gasoline, and did much other pioneering research in chemistry, and who became president of the American Chemical Society, was a graduate mechanical engineer of Cornell University.

So, when I had a young friend who wanted to study electrical engineering, I asked the dean of engineering at Cornell what course he would recommend to a fellow who wanted to be an electrical engineer. I asked this question because Midgley took mechanical engineering and became a research chemist. Another friend took electrical engineering and turned out to be a financier. The dean came right back with the remark, "If you've got a degree from Cornell, you can do anything." And that's what I think an engineering education, or any education, ought to be.

My contention is that you shouldn't have a course in radio engineering or automotive engineering or some other kind of engineering, but that you should give a boy a good thorough knowledge and understanding of what I call *informational* physics and *informational* chemistry.[2] In other words: basic facts, knowledge about practical applications, not a lot of arbitrary formulas. I think we must have facts and understanding before a "formula" education means anything at all.

Give a young man a thorough groundwork and then turn him loose to solve his own problems. I would make of him a real research man; teach him to question everything, never to be satisfied; instill in him the creative type of mind. If he knew the laws back of physics and chemistry, he wouldn't be held by specific or "grooved" thinking. He would not be controlled by formulas, nor by handbook information.

To my notion, the fundamental thing in education is to have an open mind to investigate the truth. If you get a person to understand that his opinion is not sacred and to seek for facts, you then begin to get a state of mind in which you can take the facts of history and the facts of science and weave them constructively into new development.

---

[2] Said in 1933.

Men who came up "the hard way" usually try to make things as easy as possible for their children, thus denying them the discipline of struggle that worked so well in their own cases. Such parents remind me of the kindhearted amateur who raised butterflies as a hobby. He was so touched by the difficulties they had in emerging from the cocoon that once, out of mistaken kindness, he split a cocoon with his thumbnail so that the tiny inmate could escape without a struggle. That butterfly was never able to use its wings.

Every time a youngster has to face a first-class difficulty and masters it, his wings become that much stronger. Every time he makes a choice and acts on it, boldly and decisively, he is girding himself anew with confidence and courage.

There are two kinds of courage. One is a spontaneous explosion of aroused instincts to meet some sudden emergency; the other is steadfast and enduring against repeated failures and rebuffs. It's what boxers call "the fighting heart," the will to come bouncing back every time one is knocked down. All pioneers need that kind of courage, and our youngsters will need plenty of it when they plunge into the world of tomorrow.

We are prone to toss at our children the finished products of man's achievements—the radio, telephone, a lifesaving medicine—without telling them about the painful processes by which these miracles came into being. We seldom take the trouble to explain that every great improvement in aviation, communication, engineering, or public health has come after repeated failures. We should emphasize that virtually nothing comes out right the first time. Failures, repeated failures, are finger posts on the road to achievement.

I believe that the world of tomorrow is going to be an increasingly technological world and it is the young people who are in school today who are going to do the thinking and working to make that world a reality.

We oldsters know that we've only scratched the surface of knowledge, of accomplishment. Tomorrow's inventions will make our present ones look as elementary as a safety pin. But if our children are going to improve on our performance, they must get off to a better start than we did, and head into the future with less fear, fumbling, and blind-alleying. The world makes way for a youth who knows where he is going.

The best way we can help our young folks—we who are turning over to them so much unfinished business—is to make sure that they have a chance to develop the three qualities they'll need most as creative pioneers. These are vision, imagination, and courage. Through *vision* they will see things as they really are. Through *imagination* they will dream greatly of things that may be. Through *courage* they will act boldly to make their dreams come true.

LAP-WELDING STUDENTS TO LIFE

Kettering had a deep-seated belief in the merit of cooperative education—the plan by which the student alternates between going to school and working in industry or elsewhere in some pursuit related to his course in school. He gave active support to cooperative education, both by providing employment for cooperative students and in other ways. He had a part in establishing the cooperative plan at Antioch College and at the General Motors Institute. He had an especially large influence in the founding of Northwestern Institute of Technology on the cooperative principle, and over the years he was an articulate and persuasive advocate of the cooperative plan in education.

I AM INTENSELY INTERESTED IN EDUCATION AND ESPECIALLY IN cooperative education. Since its establishment in 1906 by my close friend, Dean Herman Schneider of the University of Cincinnati, I have been privileged to be a part of and to watch the whole development of cooperative education, the form in which the student goes to school half the time and works half the time.

The distinction between cooperative education and the ordinary kind seems to be just this: In cooperative education we try to lap-weld a fellow onto industry and in the usual form we butt-weld him on. In the latter, his experiences in school and in industry touch at only one line of contact.

The plan of a student alternating periods in school with periods of work in industry or elsewhere was first used in the Engineering School of the University of Cincinnati. Many schools are now applying this system to all types of courses. I have always considered this cooperative system of Dean Schneider's as really an invention.

To appreciate the importance of his work, we must go back to the beginning of our educational system. In the early years, in this country, industry was in the home. The home was the place of daily

31

contact with the trades. The early schools were set up as places where the children could learn reading, writing, and arithmetic. Thus the children were taught the trades in the home, but were sent from the home to learn to read, write, and figure.

As time went on, the social situation changed completely. At the present time, the whole workaday world is outside the home. Yet, in spite of this drastic change in social circumstances, our educational facilities have remained essentially unchanged. So we need to put some of our older ideas about education into the museum. In the long years of technical education in the development of industry which it was designed to serve, we had reached a point where there was a great difference between the viewpoints of the young man graduating from a university and his employer who expected something constructive of him in promoting the interest of the business.

Dean Schneider, so far as I know, was the first man who considered that fact seriously and did something about it. In other words, he said, "If that is the case, why not have the young man divide his time between his schoolwork and a job in industry? Such a program will allow him to blend his point of view gained in school with that of his employer in industry." Simple as that plan may seem now, it was considered at the time extremely radical.

The medical college people were the first, perhaps, to establish the basis of our so-called cooperative education. They put their students up against actual cases in the hospital and the wards so that they might learn from direct contact what to do for the patient.

It seems to me that cooperative education is such a logical thing, once we view it from a distance, that we can hardly imagine its being a difficult movement to start. But, as true then as now, the most difficult thing in the world is to do something new. Looking back on things, we can see them in clear relief and we wonder why there was ever any question about them. But as we look forward toward the other end of the problems, they appear so vague and so indefinite that most people say, "Let's not go ahead." The past is a great clarifier, and only those who can take an aim from the past can

possibly see definitely into the future. But to see into the future requires determination also.

Why is it that we are afraid of a new idea? I don't know, unless
it is simply because we are not old enough to have got away from
our internal reflexes of being afraid of anything that is different. It
took the chickens about twenty years to know when not to run
across the road in front of an automobile. Along a well-traveled
highway they don't cross the road now. It took them twenty years
to learn that. After frequent casualties and deaths it finally
soaked in.

It is a comparatively modern idea in education that we learn best
by doing; that there is a greater development of quality achieved
through the intelligently guided and instructed work of the hands
than through the study of books or listening to lectures alone. Experience is not merely the best teacher, but the only possible
teacher. You can't buy it; you can't read about it. You have to get
it for yourself.

The constant contact, which part-time schooling offers, seems to
be just what is needed to tie up the schools with the actual occupations of the world. This is experience by doing rather than knowledge by hearing words. Part-time courses make words and books
real, by means of experience. They make facts real also by relating
them to life.

Theoretically we can learn everything out of books without prac-
ticing. But that is all wrong. Let's take a very simple illustration.
Here is a fine violin. Mechanically it is very simple. Anybody can
understand it. To play it all you have to do is to put your fingers
on it here and push the bow back and forth across the strings. If you
turn that violin over to a fellow named Fritz Kreisler he can fill
Carnegie Hall and everybody will come out and say, "Wasn't that
wonderful?"

Now, why can't we get Fritz Kreisler to write down just how he
does that? You can't do it. If learning to play a violin was that easy,
you could sell a lot of those books and we would have a lot of

violinists. But you can study the theory of the violin until you are twice gray-headed and you will never be able to play one. The fellow who practices, whether he knows the theory or not, will learn to play it. You have to learn how to do things with your own hands.

Experience has thus shown both education and industry that training for young people should include hands as well as minds. You wouldn't take four years of theory and history of music and then, after you had received your diploma and gone home, buy yourself a violin. But in too many cases in our educational work we have done just exactly that way. We haven't started to practice until we have gotten out of school.

I had a very interesting experience just at the beginning of World War II. We were running some tests on a new type of propeller which was later used on boats during the war. We were running those tests in a little 25-foot boat up and down the Gulf Stream outside the harbor at Miami Beach. We always ran the tests in pretty bad weather, because we couldn't find out anything in good weather.

Two friends of mine, down there for a vacation, said to me one day: "Why do you have to go out and run that little boat up and down all the time in such bad weather? We think you're crazy to do that. Why don't you get somebody to do it for you?"

One of these friends happened to be an excellent golfer and the other a good violinist. I said, "I never thought about that; but I'll tell you what I will do. You fellows get somebody to practice your golf game and your fiddle for you. If you find that works, let me know, and I will get somebody to run the boat for me."

You can't do it that way. You have to be a part of the work. You have to live in the environment of these things and then the facts and fallacies become apparent. This can happen only if you live in the environment of the problem.

There is no warfare between theory and practice. But theory without practice isn't much use. A friend of mine once said that there is no difference between theory and practice. There is one difference. Practice won't let you forget anything or leave anything out. In theory, problems are easily solved because you can leave something out. I have found that an amazing thing. Any problem could be solved—if only it were different. Why the little problems should be so hard and some big problems so easy I never could understand.

The most valuable experience demands both theory and practice, and the theory should supplement the practice and not precede it. The environment conducive to securing and utilizing the most valuable experience is in the workaday world, in factory, store, bank, law office, or whatnot.

To the cooperative student the job is his laboratory in which he learns the details of his profession. Today we have more elaborate experimental and technical equipment outside the universities than inside. It is far better that the student get the basic principles of his engineering education in the school and his understanding of the applications of that knowledge to industry through the cooperative method.

His experience in industry trains the student to get the workman's point of view—to learn what he thinks and why. It places him in a position to weigh the relative demands which varied situations and experiences will make on his personality, and it illuminates his own limitations and powers in coping with these situations.

The cooperative plan aids the student to appraise and develop his personal qualities, and through it he also learns something of the fundamental problems of human relations. He learns that technological knowledge is one thing, but that an understanding of people is quite a different one. The great difficulty usually is that, when a young man comes out of school, he runs up against this thing called people, and they are terrible.

Initiative has been defined as doing the right thing without being told, and ability as doing the right thing after being told once. Cooperative education develops both of these qualities. The boy who completes his task realizes the dignity of work and is inspired by it in a way that would otherwise be quite impossible. One of the very important achievements in cooperative work is the development of self-discipline, independence in thought, and controlled action. These things are essential and make for good citizenship.

My interest in cooperative education is not limited to having the boys go to school half time and work in industry half time. I don't care how it is done, but I would like to see the university and industry work closer together, because I think they should understand each other's problems. I think if we could do that, it would be much less necessary to teach trade subjects in school. We could spend more time on the fundamental broad principles of physics, chemistry, and mechanics.

I hope that universities and technical schools will provide opportunities and facilities for industrial people to refresh their minds easily and become acquainted with the latest developments in the halls of learning. On the other hand, I would like to see more of our industries provide opportunities and facilities for the educators who may wish to spend part of their vacations or an entire year in becoming acquainted with the problems of production, sales, engineering, and finance.

The intensive program required to educate our armed forces and millions of new workers in World War II produced a three-way cooperative system consisting of the armed forces, educational institutions, and industry. These programs also brought into sharp focus the fundamental difference between basic education and intensive special training. In our "Blitz training" programs adopted to counteract our enemies' "Blitz warfare," twelve million men were trained in highly technical fields. Several million were trained for the Army and Navy Air Forces alone, and tens of thousands were trained in the specialized radar and other electronic fields. Thousands of ships were sent out to sea with crews who only a few months previously were cutting hay on the farms, working in our factories, or doing any known peacetime job. LCT's were navigated across the Pacific by crews of bank clerks and automobile salesmen, and farm boys became bomber pilots.

From this large wartime training program we learned that it is possible to train men faster than had been supposed. We must not, however, confuse all this training with basic education. We could not have done this spectacular wartime training job if the seeds for it had not been sown by our educational institutions over the preceding years.

No claim is made that cooperative education offers the only answer to what needs to be done about higher education. And cooperative education is not necessarily going to supplant the strictly cultural system. But I would like to see a far broader use of cooperative education. Under it the student learns more than rote. He goes out and joins the practice of industrial or social or professional life.

Helping young people find their proper vocation in life, which spells happiness for all parties concerned, is a worth-while objective. Cooperative education does this very thing.

COMMENCEMENT DAY

In his talks to young people, Kettering liked especially to make commencement addresses. He made many such speeches, and they contain some of the best expressions of his thinking.

The shortest commencement address he made was at Washington and Lee University on an exceedingly hot day. "See that clock,"
he said on arising. "It is now just five minutes to the hour, and I promise to have you all out of here within that five minutes."

A COMMENCEMENT DAY IS SIMPLY A LINE IN THE GREAT MOVE-
ment of time. It is a little bit brighter or a little bit darker or a little bit wider than the average passing day. It marks a transition between the things you call the past and the future.

You are going out on a long trip. I have been out on it for a good many years, and there are a few things about the road and a few detours that I think I might tell you. I haven't any strip map that I can give you, or any chart. I do not think you would follow it if I did give it to you. Nevertheless, there are a few things along the road that we can look out for.

In the first place, you are not a single entity. That is all you count for on the road, to be sure; but you are more than that. I consider every individual to be three or four different things.

He is, first a physical entity, a very important thing. The question of your health and the method of taking care of it is a vital matter. If you are not feeling well, you do not think well. Regardless of whether you are big and strong or weak or whatnot, there is an optimum condition in which you can keep that physical machine, and that it is your duty to do. You can make an arrangement with some good doctor to visit him once a year to help you in maintaining your good health.

The next thing is that you have instinctive mentality. That has been the thing that helped us humans to get out of the jungle. All of the automatic functions are instinctive. They need to be watched quite carefully these days. The world is changing rapidly, and instinct is somewhat against change. Instinctive reactions have been at work for so much longer than intelligence that they always get the first seat in our mental reaction. Someone has made the statement that the second solemn thought is always essential and seldom wrong. My belief is that there never is a *first* solemn thought. It is instinctive reaction and it says "no" so much that unless we guard against it we are likely to always be against anything new.

The human race has been conscious of itself for about 8,000 years. In other words, about 8,000 years ago another item in the human mind became apparent. And that was intelligence. That intelligence was strong enough, weak though it was, to cause men to make some cross marks in caves. And from then on we begin to trace the development of the other important entity which you are supposed to have, which is intelligence.

The difference between intelligence and an education is this: that intelligence will make a good living for you, but education won't do much for you at all. When I went through school we had to take examinations. I do not know whether that is still in force or not, or whether you have to learn things out of books and then write them down. That is what I call encyclopedic education. I could best give you an idea of how I regard that by saying that if I had the twenty-four volumes of Americana or Britannica that didn't have any printing in them and I could give you a pen with which you could write, just as fine as those books are printed, I would be safe in giving you the number one volume and betting that you could not fill it. And that is only about 4 per cent of the twenty-four volumes.

Encyclopedic knowledge isn't worth much in the world. They don't pay a very high price for it, because you can buy a whole encyclopedia for $75.00 on the installment plan, and you don't have to feed it. But your ability to use one fact that you have in an intelligent, practical way is the important thing. What education can do is to teach the process or procedure—how to go about things. How to do things with one's hands and how to think things with one's mind are the great factors in education.

When I was a student of engineering at The Ohio State University, they always rang this question in on us: "Suppose you were sent to the Sahara Desert to design and build a steam-power plant and didn't have your handbook. What would you do?" My answer was that if I had a chance to build a steam-power plant there I'd have a chance to get a handbook there too. So modern education becomes more the knowing enough of the fundamental principles of the subject which you are studying, and learning how to proceed intelligently on any problem in any situation related to it.

When I said that the world has been conscious of itself intellectually for only 8,000 years, I think I can tell you a story that will illustrate what I mean. We do not want to take ourselves too seriously, because the human race as a whole is very, very young. Last year [1] Roy Chapman Andrews, out in the Desert of Gobi, found a dinosaur skeleton. The geologists said it had been there about eighty million years. And that seemed like a long time.

At about the same time Professor Harlow Shapley took some photographs of a spiral nebula, the light of which had left that nebula a hundred million years ago. In other words, the light which affected that photographic plate last summer had left its starting point twenty million years before that dinosaur was born.

Now, if we take the 8,000 years in which the human race has been conscious of itself and dissolve it into that hundred million years and turn it over to a chemist to analyze, he will go through the operations, and then will say: "That is almost pure time you have turned over to me, but there is just a slight trace of impurity in it." That impurity is civilization. If we take the two thousand years of the Christian Era and dissolve that in the one hundred million years and turn that solution over to the chemist to analyze, he could not find a trace of it.

---

[1] This was said in 1929.

If you want to get yourself into a state of bewilderment, try to think back when time started. Then, after you get that worked out, try to think of space—and that is a hard one too. Twenty-four hours is our measure of time because it takes the earth twenty-four hours to turn around once—and it takes some people longer than that. Then the year, while the earth makes its big loop around the sun, was divided into twelve months. Why they picked on twelve, I don't know, but it reminds me of this story. I went into a village store years ago. The men of this little town were sitting around a stove in the rear of the store, talking, chewing tobacco, and trying to spit through the knot hole of an Ivory soap box. One of them said he had seen in the paper that they were figuring on passing a law to divide the year into thirteen months. Then one of the others spoke up and said: "Now, don't that beat all. I haven't got fodder enough now to feed my stock for twelve months."

Time is one of the greatest natural resources we have, and one that is neglected so tremendously. Time is a great resource, and you know nature has been very good. We have a uniform distribution of time. Everybody gets twenty-four hours a day.

The one thing that education does is to put some "push" into time. I want to draw an analogy: the electric power that is in this wire is measured by two things, the amount of current which flows and the amount of push that is behind it. Now, the twenty-four hours a day is the uniform current that is in everybody's life; but education determines how much "push" is behind it. Well, education developed two things: how to increase the potential of time and also how to kill the value of it—pastimes, listening to the radio, "cutting a rug," going to the movies, and all that sort of thing. But education should potentiate time. It should make your twenty-four hours worth more. That is the value of education.

Someone has said that you have to work eight hours a day, sleep eight hours—except during commencement time—and have eight hours for recreation. I think your eight hours of sleep is the price you have to pay to nature for her contribution. Your eight hours of work is the part of your life you pay to the community and state, or whatever you call it. The eight hours for recreation is the eight that belong to you. And I am interested in the type of things a fellow thinks about when he is off the job and not asleep. If you will use that time to polish up your assets, your physical, your mental, your moral, and your spiritual ability, you will be able to handle the situation as it comes along, no matter what kind of times you run into.

Imagination is an essential to progress. As human beings we all act exactly alike. Every time you present a new thing, somebody will tell you what is wrong with it. There are few minds that are willing to make the second step and ask, *"Can you overcome that difficulty?"* But if the thing is worth while you can usually go ahead and solve the difficulty—if you don't get tired too quick. Most people tire out after they try a thing for the first time.

There is an old story about a fellow who was walking along the road on his way to church. He had on his best clothes and new shoes, because he was going to pass the collection box.

As on his way he passed a deep mudhole, he heard a poor frog croaking for help. "Please help me out," said the frog. "I have been down here for three days without anything to eat. I'm going to die if I don't get help."

Now the churchgoer was a sympathetic soul. So he said, "I'll tell you what, Frog, if you will wait until church is out, I'll put on some old clothes and come and help you out. That's the best I can do for you."

After church he was hurrying home to change his clothes, when he saw a frog hopping along the road. "Hello!" he said, "aren't you the frog that was down in the mudhole?"

"Yes," replied the frog, "I got out by myself."

"But I thought you said you couldn't get out!"

"Well," said the frog, "I didn't think I could either. But after you left a snake came down after me."

What we need sometimes is enough incentive to do things. It's like buying a camera; whether you take any pictures or not, you see four times as much as you do ordinarily, because you are looking for something to take a picture of.

I bet a friend of mine that if I gave him a bird cage and he hung it up in his house he would have to buy a bird. He took the bet. So I got him a very attractive bird cage made in Switzerland, and he hung it near his dining room table. Of course, you know what happened. People would come in and say, "Joe, when did your bird die?"

"I never had a bird," he would say.

"Well, then what have you got a bird cage for?"

He said it was simpler to go and buy a bird than to have to explain why he had the bird cage. You have to hang bird cages in your mind. And finally you get something to put in them.

There are born in the United States two and a half million people each year.[2] The day you were born everybody in the nation was older than you. The next year there were two and a half million people younger than you. And at around the age of twenty there are fifty million people younger than you. So that from twenty to thirty-five you will pass through the center of population as it were, and this brings into the picture an entirely new and different point of view from that which the people who have passed on took with them. Consequently, the average of opinion, the average of wants, the average of everything, is changed. You cannot stop things from being different, because of that factor alone.

We are forever getting into ruts. We are used to getting up, doing a certain thing at a certain time, sitting in a certain chair, or looking out a certain window. And then if you sleep in another kind of bed in a different room you are uncomfortable. The thing to do is to turn some of your furniture around, look out of another window, sleep in another room in the house, open your window twice as wide. Do something different! My God! Do something different!

You have a wonderful opportunity because in your generation we are going into one of the greatest periods of development in this country, the revival, the renaissance as it were, of the whole tech-

[2] This was said in 1929.

nical, industrial, and social condition of the world. With your training, you will be some of those who will stand out and have responsible positions. Along with those positions will come the trials and
tribulations that go with responsibility.

The only thing I regret is that I cannot be down there with you
and start it all over again. If you think that the past has been all
rosy, you ought to have ridden along with some of us on this last
ride. It has never been what anybody would like to have it.

All you young people need to do is to go out there with sincerity
and honesty of purpose, using the best intelligence you have, and
not be afraid to work, and I think you are going to find it a pleasant
trip. You have got the opportunity. All you have to do is to go out
with the idea that you want badly enough to do something and you
will get it done. The only difference between those who do and
those who don't is that the ones who do, try.

The thing that really brings happiness is enthusiasm for the
future, the things we are going to do next year and the year after.
Accomplishment, too, is something that will bring you real satisfaction. Don't think that some fellow is trying to pull you down.
You can't fight an enemy until you find out where he is. But you
can always get a good sight of your enemy in the morning when
you shave. That is the only fellow who is causing you any trouble.

The biggest thing you have got to do is to become more nearly
honest. If you are four-flushing, you might just as well paint it on
your coat. The other fellow knows it. You don't get away with it.
You are only trying to kid yourself. Don't try to bluff. If you don't
know a thing, say so.

Once I was delivering a commencement address in a large field
house. There were some 15,000 students and other people there.
On the sides of the field house were the scoreboards for the home
team and for the visitors. Some of those young people were concerned about security. I said, "I believe there have been games
played in this place. I think that is what the scoreboards are for.
What would you pay to attend a basketball game where the scores
had been guaranteed in advance?

"I know what you would do," I continued, "You would start an investigation to find out what was crooked about the game if the scores were guaranteed. Did you ever stop to think that there is something crooked about any guarantee of the future or anything you are going to do?"

Nevertheless, your world, young men and young women, will be the kind of world you want it to be. If you keep on wishing for something, a better world or a better type of anything, and you keep working down that alley, the chances are you will get it. You've got to work and continue to strive for what you hope to attain, and be patient. But if you keep your mind on your job, have faith in yourself and others, there is nothing we can dream about that we can't have.

The rate at which you achieve such things is something that is not commonly understood. These things do not happen very fast. They happen very slowly. So you must have a lot of patience. That is a thing we have to recognize in all our planning in our research laboratories. We are not thinking of products of tomorrow in the sense of next year. We are working on problems that will not be solved for ten or fifteen years, because, if we don't start working on them now, we won't be ready when the time comes.

Once when running some tests down in the Bahama Islands, I saw an interesting illustration of the practice of patience. The only way the people there have to bring their crops to market is by little sailboats. A certain man was coming up to Nassau to market his produce. On his sailboat he had some cows and chickens and pigs, the product of his entire year's work. He had to sail up the bay through barges and boats. He had to round up on the inside of the inlet where the wind was blowing against him. That is, the wind tended to blow him offshore.

He got close enough to throw a line to shore; and he jumped off and got it tied around a pin. Then he sat down and lit a cigarette. Every once in a while as he sat there the wind would shift a trifle and slacken the line a little bit, and he would take up the slack. Finally, he got the front end of his boat tied. Then he repeated the procedure with a line to the stern of his boat, and at last he had it fast too. In about half an hour he had his boat tied up and was taking his produce off.

I was so much interested that I got a man who could speak Spanish to go over and talk to the man. And there is one thing he said that I want to bring to you this morning. "Don't wear yourself out trying to haul a boat against the wind," he said. "Just sit down and keep a tight line on it." So often we want to struggle, to pull, whereas if we simply kept a tight line we could accomplish our purpose.

So you need to lay a fairly long plan and work to it. You may be able to raise some crops in a few weeks, such as the ragweeds—and of course the hay fever people don't like that. But if you want to raise sequoia trees you have to plant the seed and wait hundreds of years. But nothing starts to grow until you plant the seed. Some of the problems we are working on are just like the sequoia tree—we start them today and if we don't solve them it makes no difference, because someday somebody will finish the job. The greater the job the longer it takes, but that should not prevent us from undertaking it.

I want the man who *wants* to do something. He is the one I am interested in. The greatest thing that most fellows are lacking today is the fool trait of jumping into something and sticking at it until they come out right. I often tell my people that I don't want any fellow who has a job working for me. What I want is a fellow whom the job has. He is the one I am interested in. In other words, I want the job to get the fellow and not the fellow to get the job. And I want that job to get hold of this young man so hard that no matter where he is the job has got him for keeps. I want that job to have him in its clutches when he goes to bed at night, and when he gets up in the morning.

That is the only kind of fellow you can trust to do a real good piece of work, one whose job has hold of him so hard that he cannot get away from it. They are not such bad taskmasters, good jobs. So don't be afraid if one gets you. It isn't going to hurt you at all.

I used to earn part of my way through college by playing in an orchestra. And, among the celebrities for whom I had a chance to play was an actor by the name of Joseph Jefferson. Joe Jefferson's train was late that day, so the orchestra had to play a little extra. After the play was over he invited us to go to dinner with him. Among the questions asked the great actor was how long he had been playing Rip Van Winkle. After looking in a little book he carried he replied, "Outside of two years that I skipped, I have been playing that part thirty-four years."

Someone asked, "Don't you get tired of playing it?"

"Well," he replied, "I don't know what you mean by that. I am paid by the audience to entertain and if I do a good job of that why should I get tired of it? That's the way I earn my living."

He continued, "I think you have confused the difference between self-entertainment and tasks. I have had many fine young men come to work with me on the play who understand that I have a reputation of being an actor. We play and they hear the applause and they are very much interested. I think, 'Now here I will have a wonderful understudy, a fellow who is going some place.' But then in a few weeks he comes around and says, 'Mr. Jefferson, when are you going to get another play? I am getting tired of this one. It is getting monotonous.'

"I say, 'Well, don't you know, son, that earning a living may get monotonous, but you don't have to do it if you don't want to.'

"Now," said Jefferson also, "I only received one intelligent criticism on my acting in my life. It was at Rochester, New York, and a little girl two or three rows from the front whispered in a semi-audible way to her mother, 'Why don't the old man *act* like the rest of them?' "

Joseph Jefferson had become a professional actor by recognizing that if he was willing to do the thing people paid him to do he would gain a reputation for being a great actor. He lived a happy life simply because he accepted the thing that he was able to do as the thing he should do and made as much pleasure and entertainment as he could out of an occupation that he regarded as his task. "I made up my mind," he said, "that I would try to portray Rip Van Winkle just a little better each time. And that continual effort to improve the part has kept up my interest and enthusiasm."

If you take what you have acquired here in school as tools, you can make a real beginning in life. The information you have, however, is not a permanent thing. It is as though you had a basket filled with facts as tools with which you will work. Some of these facts will remain good for years; some will fall out. It is your job not only to keep that basket of knowledge refilled, but to do so while keeping at work all the time.

Remember this, that there is no fixity in anything in life. It is perpetual change. A friend of mine is a teacher in a medical college. It is his job to teach the young men to be family doctors. At his final lecture each year he addresses the class about as follows: Gentlemen, during the months we have spent together, I have given you the best information there is about the practice of medicine. The textbooks we have used are the most widely accepted and reliable. I have cited the best case histories I could find. But, before we part, I want to caution you that the science of medicine is moving forward so rapidly that in a few years perhaps half of what I have taught you will prove not to be so. And, unfortunately, I cannot tell you which half it will be.

The biggest problem you will have is to keep up to date and earn a living too. You have a constant problem of how to keep alert, how to assimilate the very newest things that are going on, and do a constructive job also. It is going to be hard work. Nevertheless, you must not lose that contact with the newest developments, lest you go backward. If you do not get mental expansion, you are going to miss one of the greatest happinesses of the world.

So, as you set out on this journey, there are two things, there are three things, which if you get your point of view right, you will have no trouble with. The first is that you are going to be a servant to somebody or something. The next is that to be a good servant implies two things, willingness to work and willingness to learn, because no one of us knows very much. And if, when you pack your bag for this eventful journey, you will pack egotism and selfishness and all that sort of thing down in the bottom of the bag, and if you will lay your servant's uniform on top, the passports will not have to be opened, and they will pass you through the line.

NO FORMULA—WHAT THEN?

Talking to students at the General Motors Institute, all of whom were directly interested in engineering and industry, Kettering gave the following address on commencement day, 1952.

THIS IS THE CENTENNIAL OF ENGINEERING YEAR. ONLY ONE hundred years ago the first engineering society was formed—the American Society of Civil Engineers. They were called civil engineers to differentiate them from the military engineers. So it doesn't make any difference what branch of engineering you are graduating from, you are a civil engineer in that respect. It seems to me that in the intervening years when civilian production has become so important to the defenses that things have turned almost completely around, so that now most civil engineers are military engineers.

The first engineering schools, with their type of problems, naturally had a very simple program. It included the surveyor, the man who laid out the roads and built bridges, the man who had to make the excavation and so on. And so, back in those days, we set up a type of thinking in engineering education which had to do very largely with the development of specific formulas which could be used to do calculations and make estimates.

But about seventy-five or eighty years ago, a change in the demands came, as the inventor began to create new products. There were Morse, Bell, Edison, and many other people coming along and inventing new devices. And there was no difference in those days from now when it came to the acceptance of something new. I always wish I could convince young people of just one thing, and that is that you haven't any idea how difficult it is to do any new thing.

After the telegraph was invented, the first line was to be built between Baltimore and Washington, and Ezra Cornell, after whom Cornell University was named, was the man given the job. The reason he was given the job was that he had developed some plows, and the idea was to put the live wire in the ground and cover it up. Remember that this was the *first* telegraph line. Well, they soon found out that they didn't know anything about insulation, and they also found out that if they did it that way it wasn't going to work. They didn't dare admit that they were wrong so they ran the plow into a big boulder and broke it. It would take months to get a new plow and in the meantime with the aid of some glass doorknobs which were put on poles they strung the wire. That was the beginning of the telegraph pole line.

The telephone came along as a result of Alexander Graham Bell's trying to develop a faster type of telegraph. The telegraph had been accepted and was being used, and the so-called Western Union, which has offices nearly every place today, was being formed. Bell, due to the fact that he had been interested in voice, thought that it might be possible to transmit the voice instead of the signals. Without going into any details, he finally succeeded in getting a higher speed telegram, but he also got the fundamentals of the telephone.

When they started to sell stock for the telephone, the authorities arrested the salesmen and put them in jail. They said that the Lord never intended that anybody should talk over a wire—that was an unnatural thing. And don't think there is anything strange about it. When the X-ray came along, we had almost exactly the same thing, and it is always going to be that way. Whenever a new thing is different from the conventional, you have that resistance.

I could tell you the story of the development of Ethyl gasoline, which has a history as interesting as the telephone, telegraph, or other important inventions. So you need to recognize that human nature hasn't changed very much, and if you are going to do a new thing, don't get discouraged if people don't take it up the first time you tell them about it.

The telephone was finally accepted and Edison developed the electric light and the whole electrical industry came along. About that time it was found that some of the new things could not be calculated and could not be predetermined, and so the beginning of the experimental laboratory or the testing laboratory came about, thereby bringing into use the method of experimental evaluation.

When you can't calculate it, what are you going to do? When you haven't got a formula for it, when you have more variables than you can put into a formula, what are you going to do?

On the cover of the program tonight there is the picture of a pneumatic tire. I don't know whether you have a textbook on tires at the Institute or not, but I have never seen a good engineering discussion of the pneumatic tire in any book on engineering. Yet we think the pneumatic tire is one of the greatest mechanical inventions that has ever been made. In a number of institutions that I have visited, they explain, "The reason we haven't a textbook on it is because we can't write one. You have to have formulas for a textbook."

"Well," I suggested, "you ought to drive your car without tires. That might help decide which is more important, the formula or the tire."

So there is a need in education today which considers the engineering beyond the formula. Almost all of the automotive engineering is this type. So we ask, "What are you going to tell the students to do when you haven't got a formula?"

Edison was the first man who decided what to do. He set up the first organized method of analyzing problems. He set up a definite research program and put project engineers on the problems to see what could be worked out. It is a commonplace thing today, and every big organization has its own type of research and development organization.

You go into some towns, and as you drive along the road, you will see a billboard with a map on it and an arrow pointing, saying, "You are right here." They are showing you where you came from and where the town is on the map. I think at this commencement, the important thing now is to try to point out where we are. Where are we now on the map of future engineering education?

To show you how easily you can get fooled abiding too closely by the formulas, I have been a member of the A.I.E.E., the American Institute of Electrical Engineers, for many years. When we developed the self-starter, I was asked by the Detroit Branch of the A.I.E.E. to give a talk on the electric self-starter, which I did. When I was through one of the members got up and said, "I don't think we should allow talks like this to be made before our section. This man has profaned every fundamental law of electrical engineering."

So I said, "Well, now for instance, what have we profaned?"

"You are using more current through the wires than our formula allows."

But we didn't make the automobile self-starter as a piece of electrical apparatus first. We made it as a piece of automobile first, and an electrical device second. I didn't transgress any fundamental law of electrical engineering, because those laws were made for some other purpose entirely.

We get so set upon the formula, upon the procedure, that we miss a great many of the side views. It is like driving through the country at night, when you don't see any of the scenery at all. There is a lot more country on the side of the road than there is on the road.

One of the most interesting experiments that we had at the Research Laboratories in Detroit was on one of these elementary problems. It concerned a simple beam, I think about twenty-three inches long. It was just one of the flat springs on one of the pieces of an ordinary leaf spring that is used in automobiles. One of our divisions had designed a production machine in which that spring had been used. They had figured it out and they were sure it was strong enough and flexible enough to do the work that they wanted to do. But when they got the machine running, they had to change the stroke and then the springs began to break at about two thousand cycles.

We had five suppliers of leaf spring material. So we asked each one of them to send us some samples and tell us what they thought we should use. They were given the working specifications. They all came back with figures within about 5 per cent plus or minus of the same value. They all agreed on the two thousand cycles.

They all used the same formulas, they all used the same constants, so they were bound to come out almost the same, and the springs followed the formula very well. That looked like complete verification of their theory and practice.

We then asked them to send us some other pieces of spring and mark them for identification. It didn't have to be a secret mark because we just wanted to be sure they got back their own piece. Then we gave those springs a physical treatment and sent them back. Now none of the springs broke in two million cycles. That is 100,000 per cent improvement, and yet you would have been perfectly justified in saying that this material obeys the formula and therefore you can't expect anything else.

Now I don't mean that we should disregard every formula. But I think we ought to find out whether it is applicable to the particular case that we have at hand.

I have an English friend who came over a few years ago to give a commencement address at one of our great engineering schools. He said to me, "When I was over in your place last year, you told me that you were driving these diesel-electric trains over one hundred miles an hour, and I now find that you take power on the front wheels of your locomotive. Now," he said, "you just can't run a locomotive above fifty-five miles an hour and have it stay on the track if you are going to take power on the front wheels."

"Well," I said, "I hope the locomotive doesn't discover that."

And he said, "I have the figures and the formula right here in my portfolio to prove it."

"No," I said, "I won't look at those."

I got an airplane and I flew him to Chicago, and put him on the Denver train and made arrangements for him to ride in the cab after midnight. He went out one night and came back the next, and when he finally got back I said, "I never expected to see you again, because I am perfectly sure you went over fifty-five miles an hour."

He said, "Do you know what they did for me? They put that locomotive up to 120 miles an hour, and it had no tendency to jump the track."

I said, "No, it is perfectly happy on the track. Why should it jump off?"

"The thing that worries me," he went on, "is how we could have been so absolutely wrong in every detail."

"The reason you were wrong is because your figures had nothing to do with this locomotive. They had to do with another type of locomotive which we do not build."

He was talking about a rigid frame locomotive, while our locomotives have individual trucks like every railroad car, but we put motors on them. But here was a man who was perfectly willing to say without a trial that it was impossible to do what we were already doing. In research work, when you are trying something new, always ask the apparatus you're working on whether it is happy about it or not.

I had the dean of a school of engineering come into my office one day, and he asked me, "Do you sleep well at night?"

I said, "Yes, that is one thing I do fairly well, night, day, or any other time. Why do you ask that?"

"If I designed anything as 'screwball' as your two-cycle diesel engine," he said, "I would never be able to sleep."

"I am glad I am not that sensitive," I replied, "What is wrong about it?"

He said, "It is all wrong. It is just theoretically all wrong."

"Who wrote the theory? He might have been wrong, too."

"No," he said, "this is fundamental theory."

I said, "Well, we didn't design that engine. Nobody designed that engine. What we did was set up a single-cylinder engine and give it half a dozen different kinds of pistons. 'Try these out, and see which one you like best.' We gave it valves and injectors and other things, and we let it pick out what it wanted. And to show you how much smarter the engine is than the engineers, the piston the engine picked out runs a million and a half miles, and the one the engineers picked out runs fifty thousand."

One thing engineers should learn is that the word "design" is a treacherous word, because you can't design anything that the material doesn't like. You can design things if you happen to know what the thing ought to be, but you can't expect material to do something just because you think it should. So the old idea of having the drafting room in one city where you make the drawings and send them over to another city to have the parts made and put together, and then expect it to run—that never worked in anything we ever did. In fact I think if you get two hundred feet between the drawing and the manufacturing, you will have trouble. In most industry the last thing you do is to make the drawings.

You have read in the papers about these great calculating machines. We have been using larger calculating machines for a long while. The gentleman who runs our Proving Grounds is here. These grounds constitute the biggest computing machine I know of in the country, almost 5,000 acres. In this case they don't put in something and push buttons and wait to see what comes out. They put the whole automobile in that testing machine; and if you want to get a comparison of two automobiles, you put them in there and drive one behind the other for twenty-five thousand miles and then tear them apart and inspect every piece. Those are just as much computing machines as if they were integrating machines with all their vacuum tubes, and the results are more conclusive.

When you start looking for the simple things that are important in this engineering education, the main one that you need to consider is problem analysis. What is the problem? Sometimes it takes a long time to pull the thing apart and really say, "Here is what we are trying to do."

We worked for many, many years before we really got the internal combustion engine problem pulled out so we could work on it and know what we were doing. The reason for that was that we tried at first to make the internal combustion engine work like a steam engine, and it doesn't want to do that.

In the early days of the diesel engine everybody tried to make it run like a steam engine and then the next generation came along and tried to make it run like a gasoline engine. All we did was let it run like a diesel engine. We always want to make something like something else; we never want to let it be itself.

So problem analysis is a very important thing. I am going to give you one more illustration of what I mean by that. I have worked for many, many years on this very simple problem, why is the grass green, and we are making progress on it. We know it isn't green for several reasons, so we don't have as many things now to take into consideration as we had. What we tried to do was to pull the problem apart, and we have found out one thing about it. If I lay a stone out in the sun, the sun shines on it and it gets warm. When the sun goes down, it gets cool again. Now if the stone stayed warm after the sun went down, that would be wonderful, but it doesn't. A lot of things we put in the sun get warm, but they get cool again after the sun goes down.

The only thing that has more energy after the sun goes down than it had before, is the leaf of a plant. In other words, the leaf of the plant picks up some energy from the sun that it keeps. So we said, "All right, what is the method of this energy lift?" That is physics, fundamental physics.

Now what about it? You will be surprised some day, I think, when we have had a chance to pull this problem apart and make some progress in solving it.

It is easy to see why, when a fellow used to think about a tractor to pull a plow, he would think about a mechanical horse, and he was interested in how the horse's muscles worked. That wasn't the important thing. The only thing was the draw-bar pull, and the ordinary tractor today doesn't look anything like a horse. So there is a possibility of getting energy from the sun, and you don't have to grow a plant to do it any more than you have to imitate a horse.

There is energy equivalent to 640,000 horsepower per square mile, on a day like today, falling on every square mile in this country and in every other country. It is perfectly amazing, yet we don't keep it, we don't know how. Nature has been trying to tell us how, but we are always trying to make it more complicated than it really is.

A while back, a group of us said, "All right, let's pull this thing apart and look at it."

So we had a couple of days' discussion, and finally I said, "Write down on the blackboard in one sentence what you think we ought to do."

I had to leave the meeting about four o'clock to go to a funeral. When I came back there was just half a sentence there, and I asked the boys the next morning what the difficulty was.

They said, "We got that half sentence down and we couldn't agree on anything further."

I said, "All that you did there was to indicate that we don't know what the problem is. Therefore there is no use working with test tubes and Bunsen burners and chemical balances. We have to find out what the problem is, because I am sure we have enough technical ability to solve any problem we can analyze and set out clearly."

So I think in our future engineering, we are going to have our mathematical approach that came down from civil engineering. We are going to calculate what we can calculate, because it isn't a question of this *or* that, it is this *and* that. You don't have to belong to the mathematical or experimental group, you can have them both. We are going to teach how to experiment. You are doing that right here in your school, and as I said, we grew into that because we had to.

Mr. C. E. Wilson told me the other day about a friend of his who asked his advice about a certain thing, and Mr. Wilson had written him a letter and told him exactly what he would do under the circumstances. Later on he asked him about it, "Joe, I wrote you a letter and told you what I would do. Did you do it that way?"

"No, I thought I would be losing my personal liberties if I did that."

People seldom accept advice. You haven't any idea how many people come and ask you for advice on how to do this or that, and then go out and do exactly the opposite because they say, "He can't tell me!"

So you won't have these ideas adopted completely, but you are making a start here. You young men are the youngest engineers of a type of process, cooperative education, which hasn't been snapped into existence by somebody's imagination; it has grown up over the years due to necessity.

I want to congratulate you for having gone through this school, for having reached the end of it, for having received a diploma or certificate. But I also want to congratulate you on being graduates from what I think is one of the fundamental principles of engineering education of the future—a proper blending of theory and practice.

SCIENCE AND THE
FUTURE AUTOMOBILE

In the early years of Kettering's career in industry he began giving science lectures. He found particular enjoyment in such addresses and he gave many of them before a variety of audiences, young and old. His lectures on science were usually accompanied by striking demonstrations.

The chapter following contains in shortened form one such lecture which he adapted to and gave before members of the Society of Automotive Engineers. It was presented at the Annual Summer Meeting of the Society in June, 1916, which that year was held on the Great Lakes S.S. Noronic. *The address should of course be read with that early date of 1916 in mind.*

I BELIEVE THAT IF WE WERE TO ANALYZE THE DEVELOPMENT of the automobile industry, we might be surprised to find that it has reached its present wonderful state due largely to the influence of things which we do not ordinarily take into recognition. I believe that the subject of alloy steels has had as much to do with bringing the motorcar to its present development as any other thing.

Rubber and its attendant industry has had a tremendous effect upon the perfecting of these wonderful pieces of apparatus. And it is rather interesting to note that materials of high strength, like alloy steel, should be the things of which the carriage and the engine and other parts of the motorcar are constructed; and that the thing that comes in contact with the ground should be purely an organic proposition—should be the thing which, if we were to analyze it from the pure theory standpoint, would seem just reversed.

I believe it would be well for us to stop just a few moments and consider some of the things that pure scientists have done in the way of the development of these materials. If we were to take alloy steels from the production end of the automobile, we would find the price of machines going very much higher than at present.

There is one particular thing that I want to mention, and that is the use of tungsten as a sample of what research work can do in the production of results. Tungsten alloyed with steel was first recognized as high-speed steel; and I do not believe that the man who first introduced tungsten into steel thought for a moment of what the commercial results of that very simple operation might be. It has not only revolutionized the method of making automobiles, but it has entirely revolutionized the method of making tools to make automobiles.

The story of tungsten in its pure form as developed by the research laboratories and the General Electric Company is of such interest that I am going to take a few moments of your time to summarize. There was a time in the artificial illumination game when it was a draw between electricity and gas. The Welsbach mantle and the old carbon lamp ran pretty close in their bids for popularity. The question before the electrical engineers of the country was, "What can we do to give more light for the same amount of energy?" A great deal of study was given that.

The carbon filament lamp was improved and had reached a high point; I remember in one meeting, where they felt the carbon lamp had progressed as far as it could possibly go.

Within a year or two there came along another lamp with a metal filament, which was known as the tantalum lamp. That lamp stood only a short time, because it was superseded by another one, which was known as the tungsten lamp. In that tungsten lamp the filament was made up very much as the older filaments of the carbon lamp had been made.

The carbon lamp, you know, was made by squirting cellulose through a very small die and later carbonizing it, and putting it into a lamp globe where it was expected to serve as an illuminant. That filament always had some points in it which were thinner than other points, and these thin points would become extremely hot, decompose, and the filaments break.

A very ingenious scheme was put into practice at that time by introducing illuminating gas into the lamp and then heating the filament, with the result that the carbon of the gas was deposited on the hottest part, and thereby equalized the filament. That was known as the metallized filament, and stood for a great many years.

Tungsten lamp filaments were made in a similar way, because at this time there was no other way of doing it. Very fine tungsten was mixed with a binder and squirted through a die and formed into filament. Then the binder was reduced, and we had the tungsten lamp with its attendant advantages.

But that tungsten lamp, you all remember, was quite fragile, and you had to walk on tiptoe and did not dare sneeze, in order to keep the filament from breaking. But there was in that a result which was really worth attaining, and that was that three times the amount of light was given for the same amount of energy consumed.

The history of metallic tungsten at that time read something like this: It was possible to obtain metallic tungsten, but after they had obtained it, it had about the same ductility as a piece of plate glass. The General Electric Research Laboratories, through Dr. W. D. Coolidge, undertook to determine whether or not the tungsten filament could be made in the form of a wire, drawn or cut out of a piece of wire.

The details of that would make a really interesting book. Suffice it to say that they spent years in determining whether such a thing could be done. After those years of work they had almost the same result every time; they would get a piece of tungsten, it would not show any malleability whatever; and that was quite easily tested, because all you had to do was to hit it with a little hammer and if it chipped off you knew it was not malleable, and if it riveted over you knew it was.

After a long time they succeeded in getting a few samples through, which showed its malleability. Then, by going back over the process time and time again, they found where this little impurity had to be eliminated or a change in temperature had caused it to come out wrong, and after a series of hard and long experimental work they succeeded in getting malleable tungsten.

After they had it, there was just as big a problem before them as they had in obtaining the tungsten, because the question was, how to draw this tungsten into a wire. There was nothing at that time outside of the diamond which was hard enough to be used as a die, through which to draw the tungsten wire. And after analyzing the whole field of materials, they came to the conclusion that the diamond was the only thing they could use in that way.

The problem then was to pierce the diamond with a hole a few thousandths or ten-thousandths of an inch in diameter and make the dies through which to draw this tungsten. After much work and much time they succeeded in producing a die through which they were able to draw wire; they succeeded in drawing, I think, twenty-two hundred feet of wire before the first die broke. But in that simple problem, the piercing of the diamond and drawing tungsten wire, they were able to give to people the tungsten lamp, which today is the standard lamp of the world.

I am simply citing this, because tungsten is rather a simple thing to have the commercial results which it has had. It has tremendously increased electrical illumination. It has made possible the electrical illumination of automobiles, and along with that have come many other by-products of this research, which have been almost equally valuable to the human family in addition to furnishing this wonderful illuminant. A gain of 300 per cent in the changing of a material seems almost beyond conception.

Whenever a new material is brought into existence, an entirely new range of industries is brought up; and as an illustration of that I am going to discuss a new compound which has come largely into use from an electric standpoint, but is used a great deal in automobiles; an illustration of what new products, new combinations and products mean to an industry. The product I have in mind is Bakelite—a substance which has come into use in electrical work to a large extent.

Bakelite [1] starts from two things, with which we are all perfectly familiar, from the suicidal and other standpoints. One is carbolic acid, scientifically known as phenol, and the other is formaldehyde. These two things, when brought together, form a compound which to all intents and purposes might be termed a synthetic resin, and this is not very different from some of the natural resins that are found, from which paints and varnishes are made.

This stuff has a very peculiar property; if this condensation product of formaldehyde and carbolic acid is poured into a test tube and allowed to solidify, it can be redissolved by a number of the solvents, such as acetone, etc. But if that product is heated above a certain point, where a secondary reaction sets in, the material does not change its physical properties so much. From a chemical standpoint, it becomes absolutely insoluble in practically everything known.

It has a high insulating value and it is not possible to change its form or its characteristics within a certain moderate range of temperatures, chemical reactions, and so forth. The entire characteristics of the material are changed. When in its solvent state, it can be dissolved by a solvent and used for varnishes and a thousand and one other things. Along with that development they can take this initial product, mix it with wood pulp, and by a hydraulic process mold various articles for use in the arts; those uses are so many that I would not try to enumerate them.

I have a number of things here which show to what extent such a product can be used. It is used as a matter of ornamentation, this being the top and cap of a hatpin. It has been used for making pipes—both the bowl and mouthpiece. It can be used for making buttons, and for making hands, arms, and bodies of doll babies. Here are pieces where Bakelite has been molded in certain things like copper, brass; for use in filling paintbrushes; for making up armatures and commutators; for making distributor heads and tubing, pens, pencils, and a thousand and one other things.

New industries of every kind, influencing every branch of human

---

[1] Bakelite was one of the pioneer plastics.

industry, have been brought about by the simple bringing into existence of a new compound. Bakelite has changed the entire method of manufacture of buttons, umbrellas, pipes, electrical apparatus, and whatnot.

It has entered into automobile construction in the form of radiator tops, steering wheels, distributor heads, insulating bushings, and many other things. It is used as a varnish. There is hardly an industry that this material has not come into. Simple as it may seem, it has had its place in every industry.

We never know from what angle a new thing may affect industry. I believe but few of us recognize that the tremendous development in the submarine has been due not so much to engines, not so much to motors, but to the effect of the gyroscopic compass, which will operate whether it is closed up in a steel box or whether it is exposed to the magnetic field of the earth. And if you will study that subject you will be surprised to find out how dependent, how impracticable would be the submarine operations if we take away that very simple thing.

The pure theoretical research man sometimes in his work has to forego a great many things. I am going to tell you a little about the development along a concentrated line of work which was done by John W. Hyatt, formerly of the Hyatt Roller Bearing Company.

Hyatt started out years ago in a purely theoretical way to make a billiard ball. He had in mind the making of a billiard ball which would be better than the ivory one. That was years and years ago.

He studied the subject of chemistry so thoroughly, and he had that one thing on his mind to such an extent that everything that he saw and everything he thought about was in terms of elasticity. As a result, one of the first things he developed was the Hyatt roller bearing.

He started out, as I told you, to determine whether or not it was possible to make a better billiard ball than the elephant's tusk could produce. So the industry passes on. He developed the celluloid industry in trying to find material which would represent the ivory ball. He failed there, so far as the billiard ball was concerned, but he developed another industry.

Through his work the camera film was developed. Thus I could enumerate a number of things that came along as secondary considerations in the search for material which could produce billiard balls.

I think when elephants were put in the world it was figured out how many elephants would be necessary to furnish billiard balls up to the time that somebody could make one better than an ivory ball. Consequently, about the time billiard balls began to go up in price, on account of the scarcity of elephants, the Hyatt billiard ball was brought into existence. How well Mr. Hyatt has succeeded in that, I believe I can show you here with this little instrument.

This is the original scleroscope.[2] If I drop this billiard ball in here it will rebound on the anvil a number of times, and this is a fair measure of its elasticity. So that you may get some physical conception of the rebound of the ivory ball I will just drop one of these synthetic elephant tusks in here and you will see what the result is.

I will drop that again, because it is somewhat remarkable. To show you how perfect is the elasticity of this billiard ball, I am going to put in here a piece of carbon paper with a white piece of paper underneath it, and let each one make its mark, because when it strikes there it flattens out and that flattening can be measured by the "footprint" which it makes.

The point I want to make with this illustration is this: Here is a man who started out to develop a product which may not have had a great commercial value, but in the reaching for that product he developed as by-products four or five industries which have had a vital importance upon all industries. And the thing the man should be given credit for is that he kept on until the ideal thing which he started out to develop was attained. This was made possible by a cooperative work between Mr. Hyatt, Dr. Baekeland,

---

[2] A sclerometer in which the height of rebound of an object dropped from a fixed height is observed.

and Charles Burroughs; and the constituents of the thing are a silk fiber mixed with various types of Bakelite and molded in several hydraulic presses.

There is one problem we face all along the line in the automobile industry—that of temperature. And I believe it will not be out of the way now to take just a little bit of time to consider the effect of temperature upon materials. You know we talk temperature, we talk heat, and we talk all of those things in a sort of miscellaneous way.

I wonder if we ever stop to think of the condition of a thing when it is hotter than something else. You know temperature, in its simplest form, may be represented as motion. We all know that most things expand when they get hot, and contract when they get cold. Now, if you can regard every little particle of material as an individual thing sitting in its particular position like the members of this gathering here, that would represent a body of material under consideration.

If it got very, very cold in here, I think each fellow would sit over just a little bit closer to his neighbor. The amount of space taken up by the audience would not be so large. In other words, the audience would contract. And if it got warm I think every member would move a little farther away and the audience would expand a little bit.

Now, if we look upon heat and temperature as the motions of the individual molecule, we will understand what heat means.

In order to illustrate in a somewhat spectacular way the effect of temperature, we have brought along with us a little bit of liquid air. I always like to use liquid air in these talks, because it helps to counteract by its extreme coldness the effect of the hot air which is disseminated along the line. And if we can strike a happy balance that way it can be tolerated.

I hold in my hand here a Dewar flask. The Dewar flask is the father and mother of the Thermos bottle. It consists simply of a glass vessel with two walls, an outer wall and an inner wall, with a space in between. After the bulb is formed it is pumped, so as to have a vacuum in between there, which keeps down the heat conductivity.

Liquid air, so far as all intents and purposes are concerned, is nothing but the ordinary atmospheric air which has been compressed, and pressed and chilled until it assumes a liquid form that is not unlike water—we will pour some of it in this beaker. It has a temperature of about 375 degrees below zero. If you put your finger in it you will get a burn, just about as if you had put it on the stove. Just to show the effect on some of the simpler forms of things I will take this flower and immerse it in liquid air. The simple reason that the ebullition takes place in there is that we have to remove the heat that is in the flower. [Demonstrates by breaking flower.]

We will take a piece of this rubber tube and immerse it—and that is true boiling in every sense of the word—until it absorbs the heat—stops the rubber, slows it down; it must put the air in motion and the air being put in motion, when it reaches a certain velocity, simply passes off. This tube now is quite different. [Illustrates by breaking tube.]

We will take one of these rubber balls here and put it in liquid air. [Illustrates by breaking rubber ball.] That is a new idea for golf balls.

There is one thing that I wanted to mention in connection with rubber. It is interesting to know why rubber was used for tires. If you will analyze the amount of energy which can be stored up in a pound of metal, or a pound of any substance, by compression or expansion, you will find it is a mighty interesting thing that a pound of rubber will store up as much energy as a hundred pounds of the best spring steel. It is simply the tremendous ability of rubber to absorb and give out energy which makes it useful for tires. Rubber is the most elastic substance known.

We are taking here some ordinary mercury and putting it in

liquid air. Of course, the temperature which that will bring it down to will cause the mercury to freeze, and we will come back to it later.

Liquid air's largest use today is in the production of oxygen for commercial purposes. Air, as you know, is composed of 20 per cent of oxygen and 80 per cent of nitrogen. When you compress air and liquefy it, the nitrogen will evaporate at a slightly lower temperature than will oxygen. Therefore, if you compress this, make it into a liquid, and allow it to evaporate, you will get practically liquid oxygen. The liquid oxygen has a steel-gray or steel-colored appearance. It is put into the flask in which we buy oxygen today for commercial purposes.

To show the effect of the solidification and change of materials under temperature, we have taken this little balloon here and filled it with carbon dioxide. This is just the ordinary soda fountain gas, and it is the fundamental result of carbon uniting with oxygen.

At this temperature it is a gas. At a lower temperature and higher pressure it is a liquid. At still lower temperatures it becomes a solid, and it is very easy to freeze out of that bulb all of the activity. If the frost will stay off this glass you will notice the color and the change as the liquid evaporates out of it. [Demonstrates.]

You see the balloon has entirely collapsed. That is as near a perfect vacuum in there as we can get. If I can wipe the frost off here you can see the carbon dioxide, which has frozen and collected in the bottom of the bulb here. And our balloon is still entirely collapsed. Now you can see it shaking around in the bulb there. That is nothing but carbon and oxygen.

That is the fundamental result of the combustion of carbon and oxygen. After this warms up that will form into first a liquid and then a gas, and our balloon will inflate, going back to its ordinary position. That is simply to show the effect of extracting motion from things, where everything huddles up together, the same as the simple illustration of the crowding.

I have here a little bit of ordinary alcohol. Alcohol, as you know, is used for various purposes outside of intoxicants; and if I pour some of that into liquid air it will freeze into a solid. There might be a demand for this, because you could carry it in capsules. So, some of these simple and homemade experiments may incite the inventive ingenuity of some of our engineers here, and result in some good besides a little entertainment. This is solidified alcohol. To show that it is alcohol we will set it afire. [Demonstrates by burning.]

Now, that combustion is due to the fact that we have liquid oxygen. I have a little bit of iron wire to put in there to show how you might make a Bessemer process furnace. [Demonstrates.] The iron simply took fire and burned up because we had liquid oxygen in the presence of iron; and even though the liquid oxygen was down 300 or 400 degrees below zero, immediately around it we had a temperature of 3,000. That is really the fundamental use of liquid air today—the production of oxygen.

Going back to the mercury, now frozen solid in its bath of liquid air, I have here the mercury hammer, and to show you that it is a hammer we will drive some nails. [Demonstrates.] This is made just exactly the way you make a casting; put it in a mold and chill it down. Now if we put our mercury hammer down in this water, it will immediately encase itself in ice. And if we let it remain a little while the hammer will melt out, because that water is terrifically hot, just the same as a furnace would be hot to an iron hammer.

A few years ago there was discovered a new substance known as radium; and radium was a mystery to the scientific world for a long, long while because if you were to put a quantity of radium or radium salts in a closed chamber, the temperature of that chamber would remain above that of the surrounding atmosphere.

The question was: Where did the energy come from that kept the temperature of that chamber up? It had to come from someplace. There were various theories as to its ability to absorb energy or radiate energy from the light outside the glass. And they enclosed the radium in its compartment in places beyond which radiation could not reach, but the same thing occurred over and over again. The temperature of radium was always higher than that of the surrounding air.

After a long series of experiments it was found that radium actually lost in weight. In other words, here was a new type of matter, matter which actually disappeared, and in that disappearance kept the temperature of the surrounding air above normal. If that difference in temperature were taken into consideration and the length of time and the loss of weight which was attendant with the giving off of that power were taken into consideration, it was found, too, that there was represented in that destruction of matter an enormous amount of energy, of which we have no conception whatever.

It was found that there were really particles of radium given off at a velocity approximating that of light. And when we stop to remember that light travels at the rate of 186,000 miles a second, and that the kinetic energy of the mass is proportional to the square of the velocity with which it is given off, a mighty small amount of matter given off at the velocity of 186,000 miles per second would represent enormous amounts of energy.

This radium may be regarded today as in the same line with Benjamin Franklin's kite string experiments, and the relation they bear to the electrical age in which we now live. It is teaching us something new about matter, something new about the sources of power of the universe.[3]

Radium has a peculiar effect, and I have brought along a little experiment here to show you that it is giving off an emanation all the time. If you were to break a bit off and stick it in your vest pocket and leave it there for a couple of days, you would find out that you had a nice burn. You would have the same kind of a burn that you get from X-rays, and one very difficult to cure.

[3] In a speech given in 1915, Kettering had said of the experiments with radium then being conducted: "I think the kite string of future developments is the progress already made in experimenting with radium. Most of us will probably live to see the results—interatomic energy."

The way radium was discovered was through its effect upon rendering the air a conductor around it. I have a bunch of little instruments, five in number, called spinthariscopes.[4] Then I have in that a little bit of radium chloride or radium bromide. That radium bromide, of course, is all the time throwing off those little particles that we referred to. There is placed in there this little fluorescent screen; and when these particles strike that fluorescent screen they cause it to glow. Upon looking in here, after your eye becomes accustomed to it, you can get that where it is dark and look at them a little bit, and you will see this stellar bombardment, like a million fireflies, caused by those little particles striking this fluorescent screen. There are only five of these spinthariscopes in captivity now. We got all we could to bring along on this trip to show you.

When you first look in that you won't see the thing plainly. You must get your eye accustomed to looking in the dark there, just as you might take that radium in a dark room and stay in the dark five or ten minutes, when you would see the little fluorescent glow-worm effect as you waved it around.

Now I have in a sort of rambling way gone through a lot of these things. I have one more little experiment I want to show you, because it illustrates the thing at an entirely different angle from the things that we have been discussing. I hope that none of you have misunderstood anything that I have said. I am offering no solution of these great problems, but simply pointing out to you in a very simple way some of the problems that really are, and some of the work that is being done by scientists in solving them, and I do not want you to regard all I have said as coming from me, but to regard me as you would a phonograph record.

All along the line of scientific development there is being big advance made. As Henry Souther said in speaking of the boat here, a hundred years ago we were just getting the first steamboat

---

[4] Device with a fluorescent screen making visible the scintillations of rays given off by a radioactive substance.

going. The airplane has come along, wireless telegraphy and all of those things; and in bringing those things about they have done so simply by taking advantage of this new thing or that new thing, and combining them with other things which we are familiar with, thereby producing new results.

When we were in school we all learned of electricity, how it would flow through wires, but it had to have two wires to flow on, and how glass was an insulator, and all that sort of thing. Yet the whole subject of wireless seems to contradict our earlier knowledge.

Now we have here just the fundamentals of a high-frequency piece of aparatus. It is the kind of stuff shown on the vaudeville stage to interest you. And that is going on just the same whether you are looking or not. It has been going on ever since these little particles were put in there.

We have brought about here an entirely different phase of electricity from what we are ordinarily familiar with. We generally talk of electricity in terms of 110, 220, or 1,000 volts. We talk of it in the nature of alternating current of 40 or 50 or 60 cycles.

The stuff we have brought here tonight is of a potential of 20,000 or 30,000 or 40,000 volts, and of a frequency of 4,000,000 or 5,000,000 per second. This is high-frequency, high-voltage stuff. It is perfectly harmless. You can take it over on your hands there without any fear at all. It is very hot but does not give you a shock. [Illustrates by lighting electric bulb held in his hand.]

That is the case of the vaudeville stunt of a man lighting a lamp through his body. Any of you can do that. There is hardly any feeling here at all, and I am burning that incandescent lamp through my body while standing on the carpet here, thoroughly insulated.

Now as I told you before, we all recognized that glass was a good insulator, the best known. I have here some plates of glass which are an inch or two thick. We will take this lamp and light it through the piece of glass. [Demonstrates by lighting electric bulb through plate glass.] We light it without any wires and light it through an inch of glass.

Now, gentlemen, in giving this little series of illustrations here, as I told you before, I have no idea of presenting anything new to you, but simply of showing you in a brief way some things that are being done today to further all sorts of industries, and how easy it is for us to say in our minds that certain things cannot be done.

If somebody would tell you that you could light a lamp through a piece of glass you would naturally say it could not be done. Some of these other things that you have seen here tonight you might have said could not be done.

The only reason I have come here is not to tell you anything wonderful, anything new, but simply to get us to looking ahead, because down the road for years to come this automobile industry is going to advance.

It is going to advance just in proportion as we can cooperatively have our formative engineers design new features and influence our research engineers to produce for us new materials. We must advance through scientific research in the future.

HEAD LAMP OF INDUSTRY

Kettering spent his whole career searching for new knowledge and developing new products. All the while, he was speaking up and down the nation on the need for industrial concerns to have what he called a procurement department for new ideas. And when, many years ago, he became the nation's most articulate and constant advocate of forward-looking research, the need for it in industry, as well as in medicine and elsewhere, was far from being as well accepted as it is today.

THE HEAD LAMP OF INDUSTRY IS ITS CHANGE-MAKING DEPART- ment. No business of any kind can keep on indefinitely doing what it is doing now. It must change or go under.

The ancients followed the "quest for certainty." But now we know that nothing stays definite and fixed, that the only certainty is change. That is why my favorite definition of research in industry is simply this: "Trying to find out what you are going to do when you can't keep on doing what you're doing now." A principal function of research is thus to study the future, its possibilities, and its problems.

I am not pleading with you to make changes. I am telling you you have got to make them—not because I say so, but because old Father Time will take care of you if you don't change. Advancing waves of other people's progress sweep over the unchanging man and wash him out.

Consequently, you need to organize a department of systematic change-making.[1] The Lord has given a fellow the right to choose the kind of troubles he will have. He can have either those that go with being a pioneer or those that go with being a trailer.

In business competition is more than a game. It is a great deal more serious, because the sheriff sometimes acts as umpire. In a sense, no one has ever contributed as much to human progress as

---

[1] Said in 1929 to members of the Chamber of Commerce of the United States.

the sheriff. He has had more to do with opening people's minds than anyone else I know. Industries are like some watches. They have to be shaken hard every so often to keep them going.

So many men in industry are looking for park benches along the road to progress where they can sit down and rest. But the only park benches that I know of are immediately in front of the under-taker's place. There is no spot in an industrial situation where you can sit down and rest. It is a question of change, change, change all the time. And it is always going to be that way. I think you can write this down. You can't have profit without progress.

I have no objection to the standardizing of bolts and nuts and screws. But I do have a terrible obsession against the standardiza-tion of ideas. I pictured one time the marvelous day in Utopia when everything people could think of had been standardized. There was a great celebration. Down the main street of the great city of Utopia came a parade, like the Mardi Gras. At the end of it there was a beautiful arch of accomplishment called "Standardization." The bands played, the floats went by, and the crowds cheered. We had arrived.

But if, as we marched through the arch, we had turned around and taken a look at the other side of it, the side we forgot, we would have seen that nature had slipped another motto on there that we didn't think of: "This is the land of stagnation, cutthroat price competition, and depression."

We refer to our nation as a "democracy" which is just a long way of spelling "votes." That's all a democracy is—a country where people vote for things. We think of elections as being held in the spring and the fall. But what has made this country great are the elections that are held every day and every hour in every community in this country, in the stores that are up and down both sides of the street, where people shop. They are voting. The children want *this* candy bar but they do not want *that* one. A man says, "I don't want that color on my automobile; I want this color."

Thus we vote from morning until night in this free country of ours where you can buy what you want. It is that election, that continual election of preference, which is the reason why you have to improve. Out of that voting comes the decision that gives everybody more for his money, because it leads to competition, and competition is what makes the nation run.

So you need a procurement department for new ideas. But if you start out with the idea of doing research as a pleasant afternoon's golf game you will be disappointed. It is something which if you don't undertake until you have to, it is too late. It is just as though you waited to see the smoke rolling out a building before calling a fire insurance agent.

Research can be of three general types. One is the Monte Carlo type. We take a chance on spending so much for research in the hope that the boys may stumble onto something and we may make a little money out of it. That is just shooting craps with progress. Another type is that of setting up an elaborate and showy research department, buying a quantity of fancy apparatus, then exhibiting it to visitors and having pictures taken of it. That is good grist for the advertising department. A third type of research, the only sound form, is that which really tries to do something constructive for the business that supports it, to try to find where it is going and to point the way.

If we are trying to move an object with a block and tackle, we have to have a stake out ahead. We can't pull it forward very far with each stake. And, once we stop driving stakes, then we can only pull the load up to where the last stake is. We must always have the new things away out ahead of the line, whether we can see any practical advantage or not.

So often businessmen do not understand how slowly, but irresistibly, the ship of progress moves. If the power is shut off, it will keep on moving for a while, but just as surely it will begin to slow down the moment power is removed. If power is again applied, the ship will begin to accelerate, but very slowly at first. This is not well understood by a good many people.

I was once driving up the Columbia River with a group of men.

The fish hatchery there had just burned down, and those as-sociated with it were very much concerned about the effect on the salmon fishing industry. "Our problem," they said, "is how are we going to get this fish hatchery built back in a hurry."

The salmon cycle is seven years, and it took two years to restore the hatchery. But the next year after the fire people said: "You see, the hatchery didn't have anything to do with it. We had just as good a salmon year this year as last." But when they came up to the seventh year, down went the salmon crop. And it stayed down two years before it began to come back.

Now what kind of a "salmon" are you working with in your business? Is it a three-year "salmon," a four-year, or a five-year? For what length of time do you have to know ahead about your business in order to keep it good and strong?

Research is more a process of evolution than of revolution. Progress is slow and occurs in small increments, and long periods of time are involved in new discoveries. Thus in our business, research is something that is concerned with things as much as ten years or more in advance. Anything shorter than that is simple experimental engineering. Some of the things called research, such as, "Go and ask Bill Jones whether he'd rather have a rubber stopper or a tin stopper on his beer bottle," we do not consider research. The only way you can tell the direction in which an industry may go is to be thinking of what that industry can do ten or fifteen years in advance.

I have said many times that the second twenty-five years of an industry is the real period of development. Take the telephone, the electric light and all those things which have been so important in the way of providing facilities. The first twenty-five years of the telephone was a period of fundamental development, but they did not begin to do the very constructive things until the second twenty-five years. I know the electric light was twenty-five years old at least when Dr. W. D. Coolidge undertook to supply a new kind of metal filament for it. I know, too, that in the more recent development of the fluorescent lamp, the industry was well into the second twenty-five years of electric lighting. The work we did on the diesel engine also was in the second twenty-five years of the diesel, when it was forty years old.

So many people think that science and industry are interested only in the development of labor-saving machinery. This is entirely a false notion. We have never had a labor-saving project in our Research Laboratories. The things they are interested in are labor-creating devices. Science and engineering are fundamentally concerned with the extension and supply of human needs, human desires, and bettering our conditions of living. So we are all very much more interested in the production of labor-producing projects and inventions than we are in labor-saving.

The most important thing in industrial research is picking the problems to work on. You can take the encyclopedia and do research on every topic from A to Z, but that may have nothing whatever to do with your industry. So you have to pick out those things which are adjacent to your industry, those problems which, when they are solved, will contribute something to it. Picking problems intelligently requires a certain amount of contact with people or with those from whom the needs or the problems arise. So I have often said that in any industry research today is made up of about 40 per cent working on material and about 60 per cent working on people.

The research worker in a university has only two factors to deal with, material and energy relationships. But in industry there are four factors: material and energy relationships, *plus* economics and psychology. I don't know whether the complications go up as the square or the cube of the number of factors involved. But there is no question that they do increase. For instance, it is not alone the fact that a machine will work that is important. It is whether the person for whom you make it likes it and is willing to pay for it. In industry the research man is just another kind of economist. He is trying to give the customer something better, or something more, for his money.

We are likely to confuse the *real* problem, which is sometimes obscure, with the *apparent* problem. Before the Panama Canal was built, everyone thought it would be a simple engineering job of moving millions of tons of dirt. That's what the French thought, and, because they did not find and solve the real problem, they failed.

The real problem was a biological one and was concerned with the habits of two female mosquitoes, the stegomyia and the anopheles. When Sir Ronald Ross and Dr. Walter Reed discovered the functions of those two mosquitoes as disease carriers, we eliminated yellow fever and malaria from the Canal Zone, and the job of digging the Panama Canal was completed ahead of schedule. That was the only thing we knew that the French didn't know. We had found and solved the obscure problem which meant the difference between success and failure. And yet had someone said, "Now we are going to build a canal, and we've got to study mosquitoes," I am sure it would have sounded very foolish.

Some seem to think that a research laboratory is a place fitted with elaborate chemical equipment and a great many fine instruments. But where the finest equipment and instruments are is not always where the most brains are found. And a problem is not solved in a laboratory. It is solved in some fellow's head. All the apparatus is for is to get his head turned around so that he can see the thing right.

More researchers have been hampered by too much apparatus than too little. This is because too much attention is often paid to facilities and not enough to people and ideas. In my own early experience, the self-starter was developed in a barn with only a lathe and a drill press as machinery. Also, our research on how fuels burn in engines was begun in an old tobacco warehouse which did not even have running water, and it was there that the first chemical antiknock agent was discovered.

Most businessmen say they are keen for research, but some of them don't know the first thing about it. Some think that if you build a beautiful laboratory, fill it with expensive equipment, and hire some men with scientific degrees, you will have a fine research organization. That may be so. But it reminds me of the fellow who decided to be an artist just like Michelangelo. But he set out to be a great artist before he was a good redecorator. He spent years studying every detail of Michelangelo's life. He duplicated the studio of the great artist in the most minute detail. He provided himself with the same paints, brushes, and canvas, and the same kind of smock Michelangelo wore. Then he settled down to paint. Yet, there was something wrong. "I can't understand," he soon lamented, "why the pictures I paint turn out so rotten."

In a studio it's the artist who counts, of course, not the facilities. It didn't make much difference to Michelangelo what kind of studio he had. In research, too, if we haven't got an artist it doesn't make any difference what kind of a studio we have.

So, in the matter of facilities for research, don't build them too elaborate or too inflexible—or too soon. A research laboratory is an incubator, not a mausoleum. It is foolish to build a tremendous laboratory and equip it at the outset. The laboratory should grow up around the problem. Every investigation ought to be started in a simple way by trying to find out some one thing of significance. And then let the further course of the investigation dictate itself more or less as it progresses. You always start in about the worst way possible. When you visit a museum and see the experimental model of any new thing it looks terrible, but it was a start.

It is a popular conception that to make rapid fundamental progress it is only necessary to concentrate large quantities of men and money on a problem. Years ago when we were developing the first electrically operated cash register I ran into this type of thinking. My boss was going to Europe and he wanted the job finished before he took off.

"We've got to have that job," he said. "Give Kettering twice as many men so he can finish it up in half the time." When I objected to this idea he asked, "Why can't you? If ten men can dig ten rods of ditch in a day, then surely twenty men can dig twenty rods."

I replied, "Do you think that if one hen can hatch a setting of eggs in three weeks, two hens can hatch a setting in a week and a half? This is more a job of hatching eggs than digging ditches."

Ideas don't come by the year; and that is why you can't keep books on research. One of the reasons why industrial prospecting has not been utilized more extensively is because we have used the wrong kind of bookkeeping. In any manufacturing organization you have to have detailed costs to set up a budget and to arrive at a fair selling price. So the bookkeeping head wants the research man also to say just how much his project is going to cost and how much can be got for it when it is finished. But research is not like manufacturing, and you just cannot meet such a request, because you can't expect each individual project to show a profit at the end of a set time.

When I accepted the job of heading up research for General Motors, I said I would take it on three conditions: I would have no authority, no responsibility for the company's products, and I would never be held accountable for the money spent. I don't think you can run a research laboratory any other way. The minute you take responsibility or authority for a product, you quit researching. The reason you can't keep books on research is that you don't know when you are going to get anything out of it or what it is going to be worth when you do get it.

I have taken this point of view with our people. Treat our research organization as an insurance company. The premiums you pay on the policy will be just what it costs to operate the research laboratory. The only thing we guarantee you will get from the policy is that a sincere effort will be made to keep you up to date technically on everything that is going on.

If we run a good insurance company, we will pick good risks. Those are our projects. Although we will spend the appropriation with the same degree of carefulness and thrift as money is spent in manufacturing, we cannot guarantee when we will produce income. But if we average up all the developments of a research laboratory over a period of years, it will be well in the black. If it is not, then the operation ought to be discontinued.

If the research man is told by the management that he must come under the same rules and regulations regarding the financing of his operations as the rest of the concern, then the only thing for him to do is to pick the easiest and most obvious problems, so that he can meet the forecasts. But, if he does not have to do that, then he can go to work and do something worth while by including some basic and long-range problems among his projects.

It is lack of understanding of how much time and toil are required to take a thing from the idea to a commercial product that is one of the reasons why industry is not developing in this country as fast as it might. It is my opinion that if we left it to a group of businessmen to raise human children in the same way as they raise business children, that a baby nine months old would have to be earning its own living.[2] But we must learn that to get new things going we have to spend money, *and* time. We have to have very, very great patience.

We are not dealing any more with the simple order of things. The ordinary obvious things have been pretty well done. One individual cannot do much any more. Today, because there are so many ramifications in research endeavors, we are doing things by groups—physicists, chemists, engineers, and practical men. When I started in business, I was everything from draftsman to superintendent of the factory. But this is not so any more. We are now in the second order of refinement. Consequently, it takes longer to pick up an idea and get it through to practical conclusion.

One question relating to research laboratories in industry which I have been asked by Congressional committees is whether it isn't wrong for a man to have to sign an inventor's contract providing that any development he makes belongs to the company by which he is employed. I said, "No, I myself have signed such agreements all my life. If I can get someone who will give me a laboratory and

[2] Said in 1934 at the 25th Annual Convention of Rotary International.

furnish all the equipment, electric lights, and power, and pay me in addition, and he can get anything out of me, he is welcome to it. That is all right with me. And I only hope he does get something out of it."

There is a type of individual in the world that I don't have much use for, and that is the expert. If I want to stop a research program, I can always do it by getting a few experts to sit in on the subject, because they know right away that it was a fool thing to try in the first place.

Also, if you want to iron a thing down to the most simple, commonplace, low form of mediocrity, get a committee to pick flaws in it. Why? Because there isn't one man in a thousand who has got imagination. Generally speaking, studied opinion is always wrong, especially if it has to do with a new project.

In the course of my life, I have submitted a good many new ideas to the committees of average men who do not have the research point of view. And I can tell you that the reaction is to see the wrongness, to obliterate 90 per cent of the rightness which the average eye cannot see for the sake of 10 per cent wrongness which the conventional eye always sees. So you can lay aside perfectly easily any research project which you can propose by appointing a committee of five to consider its feasibility.

When Lindbergh flew the Atlantic, Mrs. Kettering remarked to me, "How wonderful that he did it all alone!"

"It would have been still more wonderful," I said, "if he had done it with a committee."

You may perform the most miraculous experiment in the laboratory and produce a most wonderful result. But, so far as having contributed anything to the welfare of the human race is concerned, you have done nothing until you have delivered that result to a customer who may be entirely unconscious of its existence. And the most difficult thing in the world to sell is a new idea. Only time will sell it.

When you present a new idea its history is as definite as the history of a silkworm. You lay the new idea on the table, and they push it off into the wastebasket. Do not get discouraged at that. That is only the first time they pushed it off. Just get to that wastebasket before the janitor. Pick the idea out and at the first opportunity lay it on the table once more. They will push it off again. But, after you have persisted in laying it back on the table for about three successive years they will say, "Why, it does begin to look as though there *is* something to that after all!" No one can say how many discoveries have been lost because the discoverers weren't tough enough to stick to their guns and make the world believe and accept.

The greatest durability contest in the world is getting a new idea into any factory. I will defy any factory organization to lick me on the job. I have the longest wind on that of any fellow you ever saw. They can kick me in the ribs or bat me in the eye, and I am perfectly unconscious of it, provided I know my idea is all right.

Every trade in the world hates a new idea, if it looks new. Therefore be careful how you wrap it up.

In selling any new thing an actual sample of it is always important. Sometimes you *have* to have a sample. I have no patience with the fellow who says, "I have been telling them for years and they don't pay any attention to me." All he has done is talk to them. You have heard that tungsten and diamonds are the most difficult things to penetrate. But the truth of the matter is that they are very, very soft compared to the average fellow's mind, whenever a new idea is involved.

I believe in advertising. It can accomplish great things. It is the second greatest educational institution in the world. Our common school system precedes it.

But advertising is a story about a product, and I don't believe you can write the story into the product unless it is there. Powerful as advertising is, it gains its true force only as it deals with a worthy product. So you have got to revitalize your product. And the best way to do that is through research. I can't see spending 40 million dollars for advertising and only 1 million for research. If you will give me 10 million of that 40, I will make the other talk louder than 50.

Advertising men are always striving for some new appeal in their copy. Well, I say spread some of that newness of appeal into the product. For it is the monotony of the sameness of things offered for sale that discourages buying. Just try writing your friend a letter once a week about your dog. Before a year is gone he will be so tired of hearing about that dog of yours that he is likely to come around and shoot it.

The way for a research man to tell whether a new development is over the hump is to try taking his hands off it. If it runs back at you, then it has not been pushed far enough. But if, when you take your hands off, it continues to go forward under its own power, then you will know that it is almost if not altogether far enough along for you as a research man to forget about it.

However, a new thing sometimes has to be taken away from the technical men, those whose primary interest is in research and development, before they are ready to release it. They have a passion for perfecting things. This is because the research man compares the new product with what he thinks it should be. But the customer compares it merely with the old.

You have sometimes heard of an inventor being thrown out of a company manufacturing his invention. Well, I have been an inventor all my life, and I know why they throw the inventor out. If you throw the inventor out there is some chance of the company being successful. If you don't you are liable to go broke, because too often the inventor wants to invent forever, and not sell anything. So put the product out, just as soon as it has reached the stage of good-enough, into the hands of everybody and it will be further improved and brought into satisfactory shape in a space of time so short as to amaze you.

Often there is too wide a gap between the industrialists and the research fellows. Logically, their partnership is a natural, but in practice they sometimes tend to irritate each other. Your factory man always demands answers to unanswerable questions, such as "What's it going to cost?" and "How soon can we get into production?" He is apt, also, to take the slant that the research laboratory is a kind of fire department that ought to rush up and squirt water on the fires of all his troubles as they break out.

That is the wrong approach. Actually, the research man ought to be the fellow you keep up in the crow's-nest to see beyond the horizon, to tell you where there is another prize ship to be taken or a man-o'-war to be avoided.

For, in addition to the application of research to the development of better and less costly products and to lighting up the forward pathway for a business, there is a third phase which is perhaps the most important of all. This is its application in the field of science, the effort to dig into the unknown, to develop new knowledge.

Thinking men are driven by God-given dissatisfaction with present achievements. Through such men, industries are revolutionized. And even if research workers and their companies were content to rest on their laurels, you and a hundred million other people would not let us. Somehow, because you are Americans, you demand, and think you have a right to expect, more value, more usefulness from everything you buy.

So it is that American industry is cultivating ideas and men as its richest investment in the future. We are looking for young Marconis, young Bells, young Edisons. We have many of them in our laboratories now. We encourage them. If we give them the opportunity of free enterprise, they will contribute freely. In every industry, those existing and those to come, their improvements will demonstrate clearly that what we have today is not enough, and is not good enough. That is why, with all conviction, I say that the future is boundless.

"RESEARCH" IS A HIGH-HAT WORD

In addition to what all Kettering had to say about the place and importance of research in industry, he spoke often about how to do research. In this, too, he spoke out of long personal experience, for throughout his career he continued to do research himself.

"RESEARCH" IS A HIGH-HAT WORD THAT SCARES A LOT OF people. It needn't. It is rather simple. Essentially, it is nothing but a state of mind—a friendly, welcoming attitude toward change. . . . Research is an effort to do things better and not to be caught asleep at the switch. . . . It is the problem-solving mind as contrasted with the let-well-enough-alone mind. It is the composer mind instead of the fiddler mind. It is the "tomorrow" mind instead of the "yesterday" mind.

I have said many times that the word "research" is a society word for saying you don't know. If you did know, you wouldn't have to do any research. The research state of mind can apply to anything—personal affairs or any kind of business, big or little.

I have been in research most of my life and I think you can say that the procedure is entirely independent of the kind of research. The difference between pure science and commercial research, for example, is that in commercial research you dig out a fact because you need it, and in pure science you dig out a fact because you want to dig it out. I cannot see any difference in importance between digging out a fact when you need it and digging out one when you don't need it. Back when I was in college I was taught that a scientist is a man who delves into a subject for the sake of the subject alone, and that a man who works on a scientific project with the idea of making practical use of the results of his labor has no right to be associated with science. I have since learned that a bank account in the black is the popular applause of a scientific accomplishment.

Most of the misunderstanding is due to the fact that there have to be two kinds of research. One is exploratory where you try to find the problem. I once illustrated that by saying, here is a hunter, or timber cruiser, or something like that, who walks around over the hills and discovers an outcropping of ore. Now that fellow would be in the terms of many of us a pure science researcher.

Some people like to prospect, but all the prospecting in the world will not bring ore to the smelter. So some place along the line you have to begin to work the claims. After ore has been discovered, in order for it to be useful, you must have a railroad to move the material and you must operate under a specific direction. That is what we call industrial or applied research.

There is no magic about research. It is just plain hard work. I had a good friend who said to me: "This research work is the most dramatic thing in the world—this getting new ideas, originating new things. I want to get my son into it."

I said, "Did you ever see a fly trying to crawl across a piece of sticky flypaper? That is how dramatic research is. When you pull one foot out, the other is sinking in."

At best, research is about 99 per cent failure and 1 per cent success, and the 1 per cent is the only thing that counts. I have been inventing and researching for many years but have never yet found one of those storybook cases in which an idea came like a flash in its complete form. All of our work on new things has been mainly drudgery and patience, in the application of the known coupled with what I like to call "experimental evaluation."

So intelligent failure is a fundamental of research. Every time an experiment fails you ought to be careful to find out just why it failed, because the failure may not have had anything at all to do with the reasonableness of the principle. It may have been simply that you did not have a particular adjustment, a particular technique, a particular something. Sometimes nature seems to behave like the man who said, "I won't lie to you, but I'll deceive you if I can." So, when an experiment fails, don't say, "I tried that out and it doesn't work." Why doesn't it work? Let's find out why!

When anybody tells me that he has an impossible research job, I say, "If you can tell me why it is impossible, I can do it." The only reason he says it is impossible is because he doesn't get it defined completely. I have never been able to solve any problem unless it was properly defined and analyzed.

So what we always tried to do was to pull the problem apart and take a look at it to see what it was like, and from the results of that examination try to attack the thing which was least known. It is hard to pick out the balance wheel and the hairspring of a problem. But if by such analysis you can separate the problem into its fundamentals, you never have any trouble getting it solved.

A friend of mine who died recently helped me develop a dramatic illustration of the difficulty in such problem analysis. Among the activities he had in his later years was the solving of rather large jigsaw puzzles. He had developed a system which he felt greatly reduced the time required for a solution, and which technique he thought might be applied in research.

First of all, he tried to get the outline of the puzzle, how big, how long, how wide. He tried then to get the border in. Meanwhile, when he saw pieces that would fit together, he would lay them aside and by the time he got the border in, it was obvious where some of the other pieces went. By his system he solved jigsaw puzzles in about half the time that would otherwise have been required. He was thus using a simple research method on a definite problem.

But in practice we do not get our research problems so clearly defined. Our problems are always greatly confused. Suppose, I said to my friend, you let me pick three pieces of half a dozen other puzzles and stir them into your box and at the same time take out three or four pieces of the real puzzle at random. Now your system can't work at all until you find out what blocks belong to it and what ones do not, and what others you need.

A great deal of research consists in finding what pieces belong to the puzzle and what are the ones you haven't got. And so by painstaking exploration you must find out what the real problem is. But more than once in my experience I have seen research accomplishments fit together, like words in a crossword puzzle, to aid in solving other problems.

We have difficulty trying to sell practical men a research program on some of the fundamental investigations we want to make. They don't see where such research can have any useful application. Thus, one thing that has puzzled me ever since I was a young fellow is why a magnet picks up a nail. Everybody says, "Because of the magnetic field." But where are you then? I would like to know what the fingers with which a magnet reaches out and pulls a piece of metal to it are made of.

Besides the practical importance of magnetism in its relationship to electricity, which is not understood at all, I am interested in it because it has a direct bearing on another factor that is terrifically important. That is how does such a force act through space. There are four such factors that we know of. One is magnetism, the second is electrostatics, the third is gravitation, and the fourth is radiation. Nobody knows much about any of them.

So for many years I have been trying to find out why a magnet picks up a nail. An understanding of that is terribly important because it can be the key to unlock not only the riddle of how forces act through space, but also such mysteries as the valency and bonding factors in molecules. In spite of all our efforts, we have not yet succeeded in finding out much about the riddle of magnetism, but I am hanging tenaciously to research in the field because we must know something about these fundamentals, and I am going to find out. I carry a magnet in my pocket. It is an unsociable fellow, but I don't want it to get out of my sight.

All the money and all the people in the world can't solve a problem unless someone knows how. Sometimes people tend to lean too heavily on facilities and forget that ideas are developed in the mind. But you can't by facilities offset ability. This is why I have said that I would sooner have one good, thinking man in an attic than all the big laboratories and equipment in the world. Sometimes, to be sure, you need a lot of technical apparatus. But sometimes you don't need any. At any rate, when problems are solved, the solutions will be found to be simple. It is only the human brain that complicates problems.

As I have often said, a problem is difficult only when you don't know how to solve it. That is the only reason it is difficult. That is the only reason we have to work ten years on a thing. Don't think that shows patience merely. It shows the magnitude of our ignorance. Nevertheless, in research patience is a fundamental thing. In our research laboratories we have posted this motto: "A problem, thoroughly understood, is always fairly simple."

Some people try to change the problem into something else— something they think they can solve more easily, instead of adapting their mode of thought to its solution. They think in a rut and resent a change but continue to approach new problems from the standpoint of past knowledge only. But you must take the problem as it is, and let it be what it wants to be.

One thing that is likely to be overlooked in the solution of a problem is that theorizing is not nearly as effective as trying. I have always wondered this: Why is it that the thing that won't work often seems so much more logical than the thing that does work? But I was talking to a friend of mine about this logic business and he said that sometimes logic is a method of going wrong with confidence.

This is why an ounce of experimentation is worth a pound of theory. Nevertheless, a fundamental analysis of your problem is very, very important, for just trying one experiment after another doesn't necessarily mean that you are getting any place at all. So you have got to set up a theory, right or wrong. Let's call it a working postulate. Such a postulate can be an important one of the steppingstones leading up to the cathedral of success. But allowing theory to *limit* rather than guide the experimental work of an investigator is like putting hobbles on a horse. The results are what you are after. Whether or not they follow the theory is not important.

Those who put too much reliance upon theory are liable to build a confining stockade around themselves. The only way to break out of such a stockade is to jab at the surrounding wall with the knife of experiment, random experiments if need be. In that way a fellow is likely to find that some parts of the wall which look as though made of steel consist in reality of nothing but painted papier-mâché.

A friend of mine once told me, "You have no respect for authority." I said, "No, you're wrong there. I have no respect for what somebody *thinks* is authority." The *fact* is the only authority. If the machine runs, I don't care what the authority says about it.

To be a good research worker, one should have a certain amount of intelligent ignorance, for if he knows too much he won't try anything. I have said many times that a desire to do a thing is infinitely more important in the beginning of a research project than the technical knowledge of how to do it, because as a rule you can find that out by trying. We should not be either ashamed or afraid to make intelligent mistakes. Action without intelligence is a form of insanity, but intelligence without action is the greatest form of stupidity in the world. The greatest mistake of all is to do nothing.

For the successful pursuit of any project in research you have to find a fellow who believes it can be done and wants to do it. The minute you get that kind of a fellow, you are set, because you can't get him off the job. He says, "I know it can be done," and starts to work on it. He has all kinds of trouble, everything goes wrong, everything "busts up," and all that sort of thing. But he sticks with it.

So getting started to experiment with a thing and keeping on stumbling around at it—that is the one science I know that works.

After all, one of the great factors in research is the accidents that you have. You learn more by that than you do any other way.

Suppose a half dozen of us are seated around the walls of a very dark room. We are told that somewhere in the open space is a chair. Who would find it? Not those of us who sit still and philosophize about where chairs are placed in rooms. The fellow who would locate it is the one who'd get up, then walk and stumble around until he discovered it. I once used that illustration in talking with General William S. Knudsen, and he remarked, "Yes, but you don't stumble sitting down."

The fact is that unintelligent motion is a great deal more important in research than intelligent standing still. On many research problems, therefore, after all scientific methods have been tried, I prefer the cut-and-try method of groping in the dark, with the possibility of bumping into something, to just sitting still and philosophizing. An adventure to me is an experiment.

To be sure, some try to depreciate this procedure by calling it cut-and-try or trial-and-error. I said, "Why don't you call it trial-and-success?" because once in a while we do succeed. However, it is neither cut-and-try nor trial-and-error—it is experimental evaluation, and I am a great believer in experimental evaluation.

The front of development is not a straight line. It is a very ragged line. Since none of us is smart enough to arrive directly at the final result, we must work our way very laboriously from experiment to experiment and from test to test until we finally get there. A lot of people don't want to do this. They would like to find a short cut for the tedious trying and failing of experimentation. They think they are smart enough or educated enough to get the result directly. So they are very likely to apply too much calculation and not enough try-out.

Forever and a day some technical men have fought against experimental work—always wanting to sit around and philosophize, and the philosophy nearly always arrives at the point that the experiment isn't worth doing. But you can't think audaciously if you are held down by preconceptions.

So in successful research we must use all the factors—the best science, the best mathematics, the best physics, the best chemistry —to get what we call our "first approximation." It gets into final form only after a lot of very tedious work.

Once I explained this process to an educator. "Isn't that very tedious?" he asked.

"It is *very* tedious," I replied.

"There ought to be a better way of doing it."

"We admit that," I said. But there is one thing that the industrial researcher must not do—he must never be irked by tediousness. If he is going to achieve these advanced developments he has to take the best that all the sciences afford, bring them together into these "first approximations" and then experiment and experiment, because so many things don't work in the new combinations just as the old theory would indicate. When a project is set up for experimental evaluation there is not a chance in a thousand that it will work the way you want it to, but it won't fail the way you expect it to either. Researching false information out is just as important as researching new knowledge in. Throwing out old ideas and things that have been handicapping us is progress.

When doing experimental work, you are an amateur on the job. You are just as much an amateur as you are the first time you try to play tennis, baseball, or anything else. So when you take up any new problem you are a rank amateur, terribly rank.

There is one thing about a research worker—he can never lose his amateur standing, for he is always doing things for the first time. We say that in research we are professional amateurs. We are amateurs in that we are doing things for the first time. We are professionals because we know we are going to have a lot of trouble, and we don't let that worry us. But, as I have said before, the price of progress is trouble. And I don't think the price is too high.

We must be very careful how we reduce things to formulas. Formulas are dangerous because they lead us down a very narrow road. I want to tell you this story of letting down the flag at the fort, because it is a beautiful research story. The officer stood beside the gun looking at his watch. When the hand pointed to six o'clock he gave the signal, the gun was fired, and down came the flag.

A man visiting there one day asked the officer how he knew when it was exactly six o'clock—this, by the way, was before radio. "Well," said the officer, "I've got a good watch here, and every morning when I pass the jewelry store in the village I set it by the jeweler's clock. The jeweler has the finest regulator in the world, and so I check every morning."

Having been a watch man himself, the visitor went down to talk to the jeweler. His father had brought the regulator over from Switzerland a good many years ago, said the jeweler, and it's the most accurate clock I've ever seen. When the visitor asked the jeweler how he checked the regulator, he replied, "I set it every day by the gun up at the fort."

Every business has competition, and the natural competition to any research problem is that somebody at some time tried it and it didn't work. I got tired of hearing that. So I finally bought a baseball bat and set it in the corner of my office. And when next a fellow told me that Bill Smith had tried that and it didn't work, I handed him that bat and said, "Now, here is the finest baseball bat I can buy. I want you to take this bat and try to hit one of three straight balls pitched directly over the base by even the average pitcher. And, after you have missed all three, you come in and write a report about hitting a baseball. You tried it three times and it can't be done, you say. Then, just before you sign your name, I will have Babe Ruth take one swing at the ball, and what would your report amount to?

"Furthermore," I said, "you ought to have known before your report was written that it couldn't be any good. If I set up a post and stuck a baseball bat in it and got that same pitcher, he couldn't pitch very long without hitting the bat."

This is why I am not worried about the duplication of effort you hear talked about nowadays. Duplication of effort in research, in that more than one person or group is working on a given field, is sometimes a good thing. It's not what two groups do alike that matters. It's what they do different that's liable to count, because what may be failure to one group may not be to another.

Nobody can predict what the results are going to be, but there is one fundamental rule of research that we hold to. This is to finish the thing we start to do before we go back and pick up the by-products. I illustrate this sometimes by saying that it is just like starting to drive from the East to San Francisco or Los Angeles. As we go, interesting things happen along the road, and we want to take this side trip and that side trip. But go on to San Francisco or Los Angeles first, because maybe the thing you wanted to take a side trip to see will not prove to be nearly as important after you have gone farther into the country. It's like tourists buying souvenirs. Some want to buy them as soon as they get off the boat. Now, the souvenir you buy then is the poorest. If you wait until you are about to leave the country, then you will get some good ones.

So, go on direct to your destination. Then if there are any side trips, you will have a very good idea of which ones are best. And sometimes the side trips are more important that the primary trip.

Thus there is the old, old story of the fellow who went out to fight the dragon with multiple heads. He was given a marvelous sword and told, "Now, that sword will cut off any head the dragon has. There is just one catch to it—every time you cut off one head, two more grow in its place." So it is that every time we solve a problem more spring up in its place. Looking forward, then, we have more problems to solve than they ever had in the world past.

Finally, you have to be "sold" on research before you can hope to get anywhere in it. You need to be bitten by the research bug. It doesn't matter if you try and try and try again, and fail. It does matter if you try and fail, and fail to try again.

It is the follow-through that makes the great difference between failure and ultimate success, for it is so easy to stop. I think the gods trip you up by letting you have a taste of a good thing to see if you have brains enough to follow it through. If common sense dictates that our objectives are sound, we must keep on failing and learning and failing until the objective is obtained. In research, one fails forward toward success.

INVENTION AND INVENTORS

Kettering was a prolific inventor, one who held nearly 200 patents. He had such eminence in the field of invention that he was named by the President as the first chairman of the National Inventors Council and later of the National Patent Planning Commission. He served also as chairman of the committee for the Centennial Celebration of the American Patent System, 1936, and he spoke often about invention and inventors.

INVENTIONS HAVE MADE INDUSTRIAL AMERICA. THEY HAVE created millions of jobs and revitalized everything from soap making to violin playing. We have been accused of producing unemployment by too many inventions, yet the facts are that we haven't enough things to provide sufficient jobs for all of the people who want to work.[1]

Someone said years ago that necessity is the mother of invention. The necessity for invention at that time was to produce machines and devices which would save human labor, because there were so many more things to do than there were hands to do them. Today, necessity is again calling on the inventors to produce new things, because now we have more hands than we have jobs to do.

I have always been interested in the lives, trials, and tribulations of composers, authors, and artists because they are parallel in many respects to those of scientists and inventors. At the time Beethoven's first symphony was performed some of the critics labeled it as "confused explosions of the outrageous effrontery of a young man." Some others called it a collection of "barbaric dissonances."

All human development, no matter what form it takes, must be outside the rules, otherwise we would never have anything new. The critics usually work from established continuity. It was therefore natural that when Beethoven's musical personality began to

---

[1] This was said in 1940 at the celebration of the Sesquicentennial of the U.S. Patent Law.

develop along a new line, the critics at once questioned its value.

In the world of invention, our critics have the same point of view. But it is obvious that if an invention is any good it must depart from the conventional, and one of the most serious times for an inventor is while he is breaking through criticism. Most people speak of inventors as "longhairs" or "screwballs," and we are so small in number that we dare not say what we think about people.

Here's the thing you have to learn to be an inventor: You set up a piece that won't work. I'll guarantee that it won't work the first time you try it, not once in a thousand times. Then you find out why it didn't work; and, after you fix it, you've learned so much that you say, "Well, that isn't the way to make this thing." So you throw it out and start over again to make it some other way. If you stay on the quest long enough, you will make something that is pretty good, but you will have to try and fail a lot of times before that happens. So, as I have often said, the one time you don't want to fail is the last time you try.

There is no sharp line of demarcation between invention and research, except for this distinction: Invention has to do with a specific result, while research is concerned with the determination of those factors which may be necessary in the development of that result.

When a new invention is made and the inventor has demonstrated to his own satisfaction that his idea will work, it is a very human thing for him to say, "Well, that's finished!" He naturally feels that the worst of his difficulties are over. But history shows that it is only the beginning of the troubles. The experienced inventor knows that the first working model is a long, long way from what will eventually be sold and used by the public. In fact there is a good possibility that we would not now have some of our valuable devices if the original inventors had not received help from men in industry who did what was necessary to convert the crude models into practical products.

A very dignified fellow came to me one day and said: "I want to write a paper on research and invention. What is the first requirement of being an inventor?" The first requirement, I said, is that you must not bruise easily. The way people will kick you around is perfectly amazing.

The process of development and the process of invention are quite different from that of production, and that is why inventors are thought to be so peculiar. In production you have a definitely organized, tabulated forecast of methods. Somebody orders so much of a thing and you know how to make it and you can figure how much material to buy, when you can make deliveries, etc. But when you are working on something that has never been done before, and you don't know whether you are going to be able to do it or not, or whether anybody will want it after it is done, that is a different thing.

About twenty-five years ago I reminded some bankers that every one of the financial devices by which trade is carried on is as much an invention as the electric light or the talking machine. Mortgages, bonds, shares of stock, checks, even money are inventions. They said, "My heavens, we never thought of that, but it is so." They had consulted me as they were thinking of setting up a research department. It was a logical thing for them to do, something which they should have done before.

The greatest invention man has ever made, whether he made it intentionally or accidentally, is the wheel. Nature never made anything that turned clear around. She flies and swims and runs things, but without turning anything around, and the wheel turns around. If you think of a wheel as a lot of feet faced one way, those are the shoes going around. Now that smooth motion all in one direction is quite different from moving things back and forth, because you don't have the inertia of reversing direction. That is all the wheel gets to be. You reverse it by coming around in continuous motion, and around and around and around. Thus you get rid of the inertia of reversals, and that is quite important, especially when you go above a certain speed.

If you will read the history of the development of the pneumatic tire you will read one of the most dramatic stories in all industrial development. Mr. Dunlop [2] didn't develop his tire for motorcars. His son rode to school over a rough pavement on a tricycle with solid rubber tires, and he complained about it. Some of the streets were paved with what we call Belgian block. The boy's father, a veterinarian in Belfast, Ireland, said, "I think I can fix it." He made a wooden disc wheel, and around the edge of it fastened an inflated rubber tube held in place with linen cloth tacked to the wheel. And, from that time on, Dunlop's son would have nothing but the new air tires, "Because he could beat the bigger boys."

In England at that time, bicycle racing had become one of the most popular sports. As an experiment Dunlop equipped one of the new "Safety" bicycles with his pneumatic tires, and with it William Hume, who was not one of the best riders, defeated all the solid-tired competitors in his first race. Among the defeated riders was Harvey DuCros. Arthur DuCros, learning of his brother's defeat, investigated the new tires and had them put on their "Safety" bicycles. The following year, he and Harvey won all of the English and French races on their Dunlop pneumatic tires.

In the technical papers of the years in which the pneumatic tire was making its way on racing bicycles, you will find learned discussions among engineers as to the why's and wherefore's—why it wouldn't work and why it would work. But Dunlop did not let criticism or the more practical difficulties discourage him. In 1890, through the help of the DuCroses, the Pneumatic Tyre Company was formed and the new tires soon became standard on nearly all English and American bicycles.

A new type of vehicle was coming into the picture then, the automobile. But at the outset Dunlop did not have the slightest conception of the automobile. At that time he did not rate the pneumatic tire as a scientific invention, but only as something to please a small boy.

The story of Dunlop's development is no different from the experiences of many other inventors. It simply is not possible to

[2] John Boyd Dunlop.

determine the ultimate value of any invention at the time it is made. It would be just as difficult for parents to predict the exact future of their newborn child. Dunlop could not foresee that an entirely new industry would come from his invention.

There are always many young ideas growing up around us. Like children, they must be carefully nurtured. I am so positive of this that I have often said we must obtain a better understanding of the way to develop ideas.

It is very difficult to tell just who is going to originate a new thing. A schoolteacher, Eli Whitney, invented the cotton gin. Goodyear was a store clerk. Fulton and Morse were artists. The Wright brothers ran a bicycle shop and George Eastman was a bookkeeper. The developments that eventually made these men famous had practically no relationship to their occupations. But, of first importance, each of them had an idea. And, with these men, the perfection of the idea became the controlling influence.

As no one can predict who will make an invention or how it will be used, we should not be surprised when we learn that seven hundred years ago an English monk carefully wrote this down: "I have produced an explosion that outroared thunder and with a flash that exceeded the brilliance of lightning." That monk, Roger Bacon, put this formula in a Latin cryptogram which said, "Take seven parts of saltpeter, five of charcoal, and five of sulphur." When he wrote down these dozen words, Bacon probably had no idea they might later influence the whole course of civilization because, as you know, he was describing gunpowder, the first of the great family of explosives.

The hope of financial reward is seldom the motivating influence in invention. I think an inventor invents because he cannot keep from inventing. I think he is just like a poet or an artist. He doesn't do it for money. He doesn't do it for fame. He just does it because he wants to invent. Whether he gets anything out of it is entirely a secondary thing. That's the reason he gets along pretty well, because he doesn't get discouraged by these other matters.

And this reminds me of an amusing story about two chemists who were trying to discover a universal solvent. They had set up a little laboratory on the edge of town. One cold winter day a man passing in his car blew out a tire. He went into the laboratory and asked if he could use their telephone to call for help. While waiting, he quizzed the men about what they were doing. "We are working on the greatest problem in chemistry," they replied. "We are trying to discover a universal solvent, something that will dissolve anything it touches."

"Gosh, that's wonderful," was the reply. "But what are you going to keep the stuff in?"

I am one of those who believe that you can teach people to be inventors. I think somebody made a study not long ago which showed that the more education a man has the less likely he is to be an inventor. Now I think that is just exactly the opposite of what it should be. I have wondered why it is and I think the reason is quite simple. An inventor is simply a fellow who doesn't take his education too seriously.

You see, from the time a boy is six years old until he graduates from college he is examined two or three times a year, and if he fails that's terrible. Thus he gets so afraid of failing that he won't tackle anything if there is a remote chance of failure. With the inventor it's not the hundreds of times he fails, but the one time he succeeds that is important. The difference is the point of view on failure. The inventor uses his failures as practice strokes. If you play golf or tennis, you know what I mean by that. But you have to practice until you learn how. Too many of us want to be sure that we are right the first time, and you can never be right the first time, unless it's an accident. So I think educated people are more sensitive to failure, more allergic to it. An inventor cannot be allergic to failure, because he is almost always failing and it is a triumph if he succeeds once.

It therefore seems that the factor which needs to be corrected is to teach the educated person that it is not a disgrace to fail, and that he must analyze each failure to find its cause. We paraphrase this by saying, "You must learn how to fail intelligently." By that I mean, find out why you failed, and each time you fail it will bring you up nearer to the goal. That is the way you learn. Consequently, if I can teach a young man how to fail intelligently, I think I can make an inventor out of him.

Since the job of developing an invention, manufacturing it, and selling it is more difficult today than it ever was, unless I am mistaken, an inventor's need for a patent—for a good patent—is greater than ever. But the inventor should remember that a patent is not a product. A patent is a statement from an authorized government bureau that the ideas set forth in the application are new. The patent does not say that such ideas are practical or commercial or that they can be reduced to production. A patent does not protect against infringements. As someone has said: "A patent is a legal basis for a lawsuit."

All the same, there is something magic to me about a patent. It is a very, very important thing. But if you can tell what a patent is by reading the language of the patent attorneys, you're better than I am. All my life I have hoped to make an invention sometime that when I read the patent I will know what the invention is.

I would rather have my competitor think I am crazy than have a stack of patents a mile high, because he can get around my patents. But if he thinks I am wrong, or crazy, he won't even bother to check up on them. I was in the automobile starting, lighting, and ignition business for five years without any patent protection to speak of. Everybody knew, or thought, that the successful breaker mechanism in my ignition system was crazy, and that it wasn't worth copying. They infringed every patent I had, but they didn't infringe that feature, because no one will copy when they think you are wrong.

But it seems evident that the only aid or encouragement we give to the new and feeble infant industry is contained in our patent system. However, the patent system is not a thing apart from the rest of our social machine. It is a kind of self-starter to get industry going. It seems clear to me that as a nation we need an effective policy of promoting new industries and improvements in industry more than any of us as individuals need that policy for our own enrichment.

I think this is the really important aspect of the question of the need for patent protection. If the invention is to be of any use it has to be translated into a product for people to use and there is an enormous and costly step between the patent and the product. So a patent and the protection it gives can be more important to those trying to develop the invention to a commercial stage and to get it into production than they are to the inventor.

I expect to see a continued flowering of the new conception of licensing patents. The old idea was that a patent was to be used in a restrictive way. But today there is a growing feeling toward accelerating general development and expansion through licensing patents on liberal terms. There is a growing realization that in this way one's bread comes back upon the waters of increased general prosperity.

At the time Thomas A. Edison was patiently working night and day, with comparatively crude laboratory apparatus, to discover basic principles, the public was of course quite unaware that this one man was shaping the America of Tomorrow. This is typical of any scientific development in its first stages—we never know just how important it may become. And so researchers are diligently doing the same type of work in their laboratories today.

Who knows what an idea is worth? In the case of Edison we cannot judge by his personal gain because that was infinitesimal when compared with the great increase in our national wealth brought about by the use of his ideas. How can we personally evaluate his contributions? The only way I can possibly do this is to imagine that we were suddenly deprived of all those things for which he was responsible. Let us try to imagine our world without electric power lines—no light, refrigerators, stoves, radios, or other electrical appliances. Let us think of our towns without

motion pictures, telephones, and streetcars. What would we not
give to have these things returned to us.

In the hundred years since Thomas Alva Edison was born in
Milan, Ohio, his inventions have changed modern civilization as
have those of no other man. Many people say that he was a genius,
but he himself once said, "Genius is 1 per cent inspiration and
99 per cent perspiration." He clearly recognized the great truth
that lies back of every worth-while contribution to mankind—the
foundation of civilization's progress—that man will always move
forward as long as we have open minds and willing hands.

HOW NEW THINGS GET STARTED

The circumstance that most people do not understand how very difficult it is to originate new products was a matter of concern to Kettering. He thought that everyone ought to know something about the method, and especially about the difficulties, of getting new things started, and he hoped someday to write an explanation of it for people in general. He never got around to doing that, but in his frequent speeches he often referred to the subject.

IF I COULD ONLY GET ACROSS TO PEOPLE THE EXTREME DIFFIculty of starting anything new! I don't know whether I can or not. It is not understood generally by industry, politics, or by people in general. A principle is one thing and a developed industry based on that principle is entirely another thing. Heartaches and hours and money and tremendous energy have to be spent in taking an elementary principle and carrying it through to a commercial product, one which the public wants because of its great utility.

That is the tireless task of industry. But after you get a thing going, everybody says, "There couldn't have been anything to that. Look how well it works now." It is like looking through a telescope the wrong way.

A long history of patient experimentation lies back of these things that made them so easy to get. You can buy the incandescent electric lamp in any store for ten or fifteen cents.[1] Yet there is perhaps no one simple thing in the world that had as much work put on it as that lamp. It is nothing but a piece of wire in a bottle. That is all. But that simple thing of putting a wire in a bottle has been one of the most enormously useful things that the world has ever seen. Yet to get that piece of wire in a bottle to stand the high heat, to give off good light, and to have a long life took more

---

[1] Said in 1937.

man-hours of experimentation than perhaps any other simple thing. That is the part you don't see.

The long period of experimentation on the electric lamp began with the patient search of Thomas A. Edison for a suitable carbon filament for his pioneer incandescent lamp. For eighteen to twenty hours a day he experimented with all sorts of materials, from human hair to plant fiber from the South Seas, until one day he found that carbonized bamboo fiber gave the best results. Most people would have stopped there, but not Edison. He had to find the best type of fiber. He had men search the forests of Cuba, Jamaica, Ceylon, and Burma for vegetable fiber and grass. He tested more than 6,000 such materials, and his investigations on this one thing alone cost a small fortune.

For some years after the coming of the carbon-filament electric lamp, as I have mentioned before, the electric lighting business and the gas lighting business were running along neck and neck—but with the gas people drawing ahead a little bit every so often. When someone proposed that what was needed was a far better electric lamp, one giving two or three times as much light for the same current, the electric light people actually thought that any increase in the amount of light a lamp gave would be a bad thing for the power station. People would expect to get the extra light for the same old price—and then where would the electric light people be? They did not have the imagination to see that people would use more electric light than they had ever thought of using if it could be made a better light than they had been able to get up to that time.

Someone who was persistent finally found out how to make filaments of tungsten. He was a long time at it and there were plenty of discouragements, but at last he found out how to do the trick. Right then the electric light industry passed the gas lighting people, and they have hardly been heard of since that time.

Thus, that putting of a wire in a bottle was the beginning of a great industry. It developed and is still developing. So you never can tell when you see these simple experiments being performed what will become of them.

I, personally, as a member of an industrial research organization, wish to pay tribute to Thomas A. Edison as a pioneer organizer of a research group. In 1870, after he had received payment for improving the stock ticker, he set up business in Newark, New Jersey. Perhaps it was not so clearly evident to the young Edison as it is to us nowadays just how difficult it is to conduct research, engineering, and manufacturing all under one roof. We realize today that these are three distinct stages in converting an idea into reality, and the time interval separating each of these stages may run into years.

Edison's keen mind, however, quickly grasped the fact that something was wrong. He could not develop his ideas and manufacture things with the same facilities. So he turned over the factory to a competent superintendent and moved to Menlo Park where he could concentrate undisturbed on ideas.

But he had more new ideas than he had time and hands to work out. As a result, he made what was probably one of his greatest contributions to mankind—he collected around him a group of brilliant men who could help him explore the many channels opened by his fertile mind. Today such organized research is the basis of most technical progress, and we owe a great debt to the man who led the way over eighty years ago.

So in this country we have developed an experimental method of getting new things. They come directly from a system called industrial research—a process which is American through and through. An inventor or scientist working in a small way gets an idea and from this comes a very simple working model. This is then tried out and a little larger or better one is made. Finally, the engineers design it into a product. Some samples are made and tried out in the hands of users. If this is satisfactory, the device or material is put into limited production. It may take ten or fifteen years from the time the idea started before it is put into general use.

Back of each new product you will find the same story of hard work, patience, and disappointment. Research men, inventors, and engineers must spend time thinking of new ideas, developing them, experimenting with them to perfect their samples, just as the authors or composers must get an idea or theme, write it one way, change it, cut and try, and then do the whole thing over again and again before they are satisfied.

Thus ideas grow very much like plants. In the first place, the ground must be right. You have to plant the seed, and when it first comes through the ground it is quite tender and vulnerable, and the proper care of the plant in this state is very important if it is to live and grow. It must be cultivated, and the weeds of prejudice and immobility of mind cleared away, for prejudice and precedent are the two watchdogs at the gate of progress.

When you are going into new work, I can tell you that one of the biggest jobs you will have is to strong-arm the opposition of well-meaning people. That has been universally true everywhere and with everything. In putting out new things troubles are not the exception. They are the rule.

It has been my good fortune to have had the opportunity to go through at least a dozen of these new developments. Two or three of them were chemical, others electrical, still others mechanical, and the life histories of all were very much the same.

There is a period in all these developments which I have elected to call the "shirt-losing zone," because you can surely lose your shirt in it about as easily as anywhere I know. This is the development stage, the long period between the time you have the idea until you can put it into a factory on a profit-and-loss basis. Or it may be the time, after you have put the article on the market and the public have started to buy it, when—either through competition or through misuse—it gets a serious setback. This is the most dangerous period and I am sure, after having had this rather large number of experiences, that many good ideas must have failed at this point. Industry doesn't understand this growth period, although we understand the growth period in every other thing.

When the telegraph was invented it created a new industry. That new industry was important so far as it absorbed people and created new jobs. But that was of no importance at all compared to the secondary results. With the telegraph we had a new method of communication. People began to change their methods of doing business. We needed more telegrams, so we needed more wires; we needed more people, we needed more and more of everything that had to do with the telegraph business.

The first telegraph message was: "What hath God wrought?" That was interesting. It was a nice thing to do and a nice thing to recognize. But that wasn't the reason they sent that message. They were surprised that their outfit was as good as it was. The Lord had helped, as He always does. So the inventor just spoke out in plain English, all tickled, "What hath God wrought?"

But at first nobody could see any use for the telegraph, because why should anybody be in such a hurry about getting information? But it happened that there was going to be an election that year. Some politicians got a wise idea, and they used the telegraph to send word to Washington that if they nominated a certain fellow everything would be all right. The information got there ahead of the other politicians who went down on the train to prevent such a nomination. When the politicians arrived they found that the thing was already fixed through communication by telegraph. You see how politics played its part even in technological development.

After that the telegraph started to move. Today you can send a message around the world in about one-seventh of a second—if you have one worth sending around the world.

One of my first jobs was with a little telephone company in Ashland, Ohio. So I am full of admiration for what has been done with the telephone. I remember when it was regarded as a piece of luck if you succeeded in carrying on a conversation across town. Now, I can pick up that instrument and talk to a friend in Paris or London or Madrid, or I can join in a conference with a dozen persons talking from as many different cities. I can talk with any one of hundreds of millions of people, and the range is widening.

The telephone company has a remarkably well-organized system for attacking its problems as they arise, or even before they arise.

So, in the course of only a few years, they have made improvements that would have come along only after many years, if ever, if no systematic research had been conducted.

Out of the desire to improve and perfect the telephone came the radio. Eventually, other communication devices were added. They began to send pictures by telegraph, called sound pictures or wire photos, another type of telegraphy. Now, when something happens in another part of the world, pictures are sent by radio and are reproduced from a machine at their destination. That's the way things happen. Nobody can predict these things. At the outset nobody could anticipate the possibility of projecting a voice across the United States by telegraph, and so no such industry could be planned. But everything which improves a given product makes possible development and progress in an allied product.

A great industrialist once said to me: "The thing I don't like about you research fellows is that you don't do a good enough first job."

"What do you mean by that?" I asked.

"You develop a new product and we put it on the market and then you have to change and change and change before you get it into a satisfactory product."

"You're right," I said. "I think the jobs that we do in the research laboratory are just the kind that any amateurs would be expected to do."

"But you're not an amateur," he said. "Look at the facilities you've got."

"Well," I said, "What is an amateur? He is a fellow who is doing something for the first time. You can't make the second model without making the first. So you have to make the first one, even if it isn't very good. When a fellow is learning a new language he still speaks with the accent of the old. And on new endeavors we have to strive to get rid of the old accent."

"Do you play golf?" I asked him.

"No," he replied.

"Well, I am going to get you the best set of golf clubs I can buy, and I am going to expect you to break a hundred the first time you try to play the game."

"Why, that's unreasonable," he said. "Before you can do that you have to practice and practice and practice."

And that is exactly how it is with originating a new thing or an industry. You have to practice and those changes you object to are just the practice. After you put a new product out into the field, people begin to use it in different ways from what you expected and it's got to be changed. And so over a period of years a product grows.

We think we can plan an industry, but we can't because you can't tell whether something is going to be an industry or not when you see it. And the chances are that it grows up right in front of you without ever being recognized as an industry.

Certainly I know that Oersted did not know he was creating an industry when he held an electric wire over a compass needle and found that it was deflected. He searched for that for a long while. Michael Faraday went a little further. He wound a coil and discovered the fundamentals of electrical induction upon which our whole electrical and communications business is based.

Joseph Henry in this country was a contemporary in the development of the magnet. But in that simple thing of winding a coil on a bar of iron the fundamental principle of the telegraph was developed. And our S. F. B. Morse, taking that as a clue, succeeded in developing the principles of our present telegraph.

But the electrical thought has been growing for over 2,500 years. It really started as a very weak, vague idea in the year 600 B.C., when a Greek philosopher, Thales of Miletus, found that by rubbing amber he produced a force that would pick up straws. Two thousand years later, Sir William Gilbert, Queen Elizabeth's physician, did a little more thinking and experimenting with the idea and called the phenomenon *electricity*. One hundred years later, Benjamin Franklin identified positive and negative electricity and proved that lightning and electricity were the same thing. Then, in 1820, Oersted, a Dane, proved that electricity would produce magnetism. And, about the same time, Faraday did some experimenting and discovered the principles of the electric motor.

After Faraday, came Morse and Bell, who used the idea as means of communication—the telegraph and the telephone. Edison made the idea glow and lit up the world. Marconi and De Forest went Morse and Bell one better and laid the foundation for radio. Thus was the electrical idea carefully cultivated and expanded by a few straight-thinking men—a Greek, an Englishman, a German, a Dane, an American, and an Italian. Often these men were working at the same time, unknown to each other. And this small, apparently unimportant idea in the year 600 B.C. has grown until it has literally changed the face of the earth and the habits of its people.

Who planned the automobile industry, if you please? It grew in spite of planning. I have always said that had it not been for alloy steel, rubber, and petroleum, you could have had no automobile business, and certainly you couldn't have had an automotive industry if it hadn't been for the rubber tire.

I have enjoyed the comfort of air conditioning in my house since it was built many years ago. I could not get the architect or the contractor to give me what I wanted. They threw up their hands at my suggestion. They knew it was possible to make ice, of course. In actuality, I personified at that time a great potential market for this aid to comfortable living. But they put me down as a visionary. So I bought what was needed to apply a well-established scientific principle and made my own air-conditioning plant. That is just one compensation of being an independent sort of mechanic.

You know the story of Radio Station KDKA in Pittsburgh, one of the first broadcasting stations in the country. How did it come into being? Was it organized by a great bank with unlimited resources? No. It was started by a fellow who thought he could play a phonograph record that his neighbors would like to hear. It grew because it provided a service which was worth more to people than what they paid for it. That is the secret of the success of any industrial organization.

The radio, with its principles developed far in advance of our present vacuum tubes, became an industry almost overnight. Another interesting thing is that in that technical study made by the amateurs who sat up all night to try to telegraph across the street, you had developed the technicians who made the service men. Radio became an operating facility rapidly because of the ready availability of those trained men who had been the amateurs. They were self-educated.

Why did they want to study radio? Because they wanted to go into the business? No, they hadn't any idea it was a business. It was something they wanted to do. It was an adventure. What did they expect to get out of it? They hadn't any idea. It was something that looked as though it needed to be done and they wanted to do it.

I doubt whether anybody was ever conscious of creating an industry at the time it was started. I have even said that nobody is smart enough to go into the business he ends up in. You get into an industry without knowing it. Economic planning is like predicting the Kentucky Derby. You are very likely to bet on the wrong horse.

About a hundred years ago there was broken off from the cliff of knowledge, if you want to think of it as such, a great chunk of fundamental scientific information which fell down here into a level place. It was out of that piece of basic material that the engineer has been busy fabricating a great many of the so-called modern developments in all the basic scientific and engineering subjects. It was the building of the railroads, the making of industries, the extension of the use of electricity for communication, and of the other modern developments that we have been getting out of that native piece of rock which was blasted from the cliff a hundred years ago.

We got so interested in the fabrication of that primary informa-

tion into usable products that I think we forgot that maybe it was
an accident that the information broke off when it did. We haven't
been giving enough concern to getting a new piece of rock, after
the first one was nearly used up, as we have in fabricating the things
which we already possess. Consequently, we have been so busy
formalizing the method by which we had cut up that first piece of
rock that we failed to recognize that this formularizing is not good
after the basic material is used up.

Labor and material aren't the only items that go into an article.
We get so interested in the material phases that we miss the
intangible something that goes into it. I have often used the radio
as an illustration of that. This little incident happened some years
ago in my home in Dayton. We were sitting there, and we tuned
the radio in on London. Pretty soon an English voice said, "This
is London speaking."

A friend of mine who was present said, "Why, that is marvelous!
I can't understand that. I can't understand this radio at all."

"Well," I said, "let's analyze this thing. If it is wonderful, we
ought to be able to take it apart and find the wonder in it. We
take the set out of its case and say to the furniture manufacturer,
'Can you make these cabinets for us?'

"He says, 'Sure, I can make those by the thousand. How many
do you want?'

"We say to the electrical people, 'Can you make these tubes?'

" 'Yes, by the millions. We can make those condensers, those
coils, those switches too.

"Anybody can make those pieces. And, when the radio set is
thus broken down piece by piece, it doesn't seem at all marvelous.
What did you say it was?"

"The reason I said it was wonderful," he replied, "was that I
could hear London."

"That isn't the material and the labor alone," I said. "No amount
of labor and material could let you hear 'This is London calling'
if it wasn't for the boiled-down essence of knowledge from every

great electrical engineer and physicist since the time of Michael Faraday scooped up together and put into that package. That is what is housed in the radio cabinet along with so many pounds of material—that intangible something which goes into every product, that something which is priceless."

To illustrate how priceless it is, let us suppose that there was some force that could take radio away, could completely wipe out radio in the world. What would it be worth to have a group of men rediscover and redevelop that intangible something—the something which makes it possible to take a few pounds of material and a few hours of work and with it be in contact with almost any place in the world?

So the thing that really started progress and that maintains it in the world is man's ability to think, and his dissatisfaction with things as they are. That is the intangible motive power which makes for human progress.

It is that important factor which we sometimes overlook. But the progress we have made from the time of Michael Faraday to the present is only a step on the road of eternal progress that will be made just as long as men will think ahead.

OBSERVATIONS ON ENGINEERS

*As an engineer, Kettering often talked about the profession—
about its importance, about the education and qualities needed for
the practice of it, and about the obligations and achievements of
engineers, as well as about their shortcomings and their blunders.*

SOMEBODY ASKED ME ONCE, "WHAT IS THE DIFFERENCE BE-
tween a scientist and an inventor or engineer?"

"Well," I said, "if you are looking at a great loom, the threads
running lengthwise in the loom, which we call the warp, represent
the scientists, the physicists, the chemists, and so on. These can
be highly specialized. But you can't make a fabric out of just the
warp alone. You have to have the shuttle to put in cross threads,
called the woof. The woof, in which the threads run at right angles
to those of the warp, represents the work of the inventor or the
engineer who ties together all the sciences. If you don't think the
engineer has a useful part, just try to sleep in a purely scientific
hammock and see what happens."

Science is an idea. It is making a discovery or putting together
a new combination of things. But technology or engineering is
delivering that idea or device to the public at a price which they
can afford to pay, or which it is worth while for them to pay.

Engineering must partake as much of economic horse sense as
it does of scientific principles; because, in the end, it is merely the
adaptation of fundamental materials to the utility of mankind. If
the cost of this transfer is more than the public will pay, the
proposition is doomed to failure and all the scientific theories in the
world will not save it. Engineering is thus a combination of brains
and material—the more brains the less material.

We've always said that we are great believers in the fourth
dimension. Most engineering problems consist of length, of breadth
and thickness, and our fourth dimension is cost. We feel that,
instead of calling cost the fourth dimension, it should be the first

dimension, because we have got to design against cost continually
if we are going to get a product which will meet the requirements
in the field.

We are so used to all this work that civilization has done, these
wonderful railroad trains, skyscrapers, ships, and all that kind of
thing, that sometimes we forget that they have just been built for
people to use. That is all. If we were all twice as big as we are,
this building would have to be twice as big, these tables and chairs
would have to be bigger. If we were only one-half the size, they
would not need to be so large. But practically everything that
civilization has produced has taken the form it has because of the
average size and form of a human being. If you want to confuse
civilization, just bend the knee joints the other way and see what
you get into.

The fundamental laws of nature don't care what we think about
them. The greatest shortcoming which some people have is to
think they can edict something. The only thing you can do is to
follow things. That is the only way you get things done.

I have often told this story about the time when we were first
developing an improved diesel engine. Just for fun we put a
couple of pistons on display before the Society of Automotive
Engineers. One piston was conventional in form and the other
newly developed and quite different. In the exhibit were cross
sections of the pistons and cards saying how long each would run
without service, and giving other data.

I dropped in there one evening and a fellow I knew came over
and said, "I wouldn't have that piston you fellows are using in an
engine of mine."

"Why not?" I asked. "Look at the card for that piston. It runs
thirty times as long without trouble as the other one, the conventional one."

"Well," he said, "I can tell by looking at that new piston that it's
no good."

"How can you tell that?" I asked.

"I am an engineer," he said.

"But were you ever a piston in a diesel engine?" I replied. "That original piston had been yelling at the top of its voice that things were not right with it."

A principle that we have tried to impress upon our young fellows is that the good engineer is the fellow who lets the job be his boss. What does the engineer think of this new piston? That doesn't matter. What does the engine think about it? That does matter. The engineer's opinion is worth very little. The engine's opinion is worth a great deal. If the engine says, "I like this piston," and it happens to be contrary to the engineer's pet idea, that's too bad. It simply proves that the engineer was wrong. So quit trying to tell the engine what it ought to do and let it do the talking. After all, the only reason for all this expensive research is that it corrects our ignorance factor so that we can see the problem in its true light.

I object to the belief that engineering is a mathematical science. It is an experimental science. I have been in the engine business for a great many years, and if you are going to build just one big engine, then you have to rely completely on calculations. So then we put in those clever things we call "factors of safety."

A good engineer likes to have a good generous factor of safety. Well, a factor of safety of ten means that you guess your figures are about 10 per cent right. That is all. So we have changed the name and call it factor of ignorance. It is just a clever contrivance, like that which bankers have when they say they "accommodate" you when they loan you money. All professions have their clever little nomenclatures. The factor of safety is one that got into engineering.

But when you can use the method of experiment, where you can make a few models and run them and break them up and fix them again, that is the easy kind of engineering. Without that opportunity for trial, it is pretty hard to design a diesel engine when you have never been a part of one yourself, because you can only assume that the stresses have been so and so.

The factor that makes an important difference is sometimes an elementary one. A number of years ago we had occasion to develop a special crankshaft testing machine for measuring fatigue life in engine crankshafts. We broke some twenty of these shafts and in so doing found that we could improve the fatigue life of the shaft by 1,000 per cent. All we did was to change the heat-treat temperature in one of the routines by 400 degrees and drill an oil hole at a different place. Neither one of those items had been taken into consideration at all by the designer of the shaft, but they were very important factors.

When some years ago we began our effort to develop an automobile engine of really high compression, I gave the job to a group of young engineers. They had been at the work only a week when they came to me and said, "Boss, we want you to write a letter saying that we are working on this engine because you asked us to, not because we want to."

"What do you want a letter for?" I asked.

"Because this is theoretically wrong," they replied.

"Who wrote the theory?" I said. "I will write the letter you ask for, but I won't sign it. If this is as bad as you say it is, nobody is going to hear about it. If it is as good as I think it is, everybody is going to hear about it. But, for God's sake, let the engine decide. Stop butting in ahead of time."

Which brings me to another thing, and that is that the customer runs this country, not the management, not the engineers. The best and most successful companies are those that run the best errands for their customers. And the engineer who is successful is the fellow who has run the best errands for his company or their projects.

One place where we make a mistake is in going ahead and developing something which is just a little bit too far ahead. It does not quite hitch up. I illustrate that by saying: Here is a wonderful Pullman train all ready to go. We cannot use that train at all. The engine must first back up to where the old and the new may meet. They say, "No, we won't do that. We will not belittle ourselves by backing up and coupling on." So we refuse to simplify the thing down to the point where the average man can use it.

We have a great alibi for the lack of psychology in industry, and that is the instruction book. We say the instruction book is the engineer's alibi. The bigger the instruction book, the less the engineer knows about the people who are going to use his product. The man who can put out a piece of apparatus without an instruction book is the man who has a complete and comprehensive knowledge of the psychology of his users.

Here is a pistol. You lay it down and another man comes along and takes hold of it. You do not need to give him an instruction book. But suppose you made one that you had to hold upside down in order to shoot. I do not care how wonderful it is, it would be a commercial failure, no matter if you tied to it eleven instruction books.

Make the device so the public can't use it wrongly, because they are the ones who are paying your board bill. In other words, going out and satisfying the public is the job of the engineer, and it doesn't make any difference how the public wants that thing, they are going to get it the way they want it. You will find it is much easier to give it to them the way they want to use it than to try forcing them to use it the way you want it. The reputation of a motorcar is made in the used car market after the instruction book is lost. So I am for very, very thin instruction books.

Shortly after World War II an admiral in the Navy, speaking to a group of young Navy engineers, said: "We came through the war and we did a pretty good job with the Navy. But now our battleships, our submarines, our destroyers, and our aircraft carriers are no good.

"What kind of a Navy are we going to have in the future? Are we going to have a push-button Navy? The General Staff has been working on that day and night and Sundays, in fact, and we have gone further than anybody thinks." Then, putting his hand into his pocket, pulling out a push button, and holding it up, the Admiral said: "We have the job half done already and here it is."

"Now," he continued, "what is going to go on the other side of this push button I don't know. And when we are going to get it I don't know. But, while we are waiting for that development, don't you think it would be a good thing to clean up the battleships, the submarines, and the destroyers, because some of those prophecies may take a thousand years to come true."

Engineers as a class are too conceited. They think they know a lot. They don't mix enough with different kinds of people. They lack imagination. They are not emotional enough. Few of them have broad mental perspective. Too many of them are satisfied with things as they are. They are not dissatisfied enough. They are inclined to put formulas ahead of facts, and most of them lack the ability to transfer their thoughts in simple language to the general public.

A man's language, as a rule, is an index of his mind. A clearly written paper or report indicates sound reasoning and reliable results. One of the greatest mistakes that engineers make in writing and talking is that they speak in the language of their trade and not in the language of their listeners or readers. As a rule engineers so like to use their high-sounding Latin and Greek derivatives that they leave their listeners completely confused, when they could have told the same story in words understood perfectly by everybody in their audience.

Recently a friend of mine attended a luncheon at which a man talked on "the probable methods of the inhibitions of corrosion in ferrous materials." When I asked him what he thought about the speech, he said, "Heck, I thought the fellow was going to talk about how to stop rust in iron." It is perfectly possible to write about an abstract subject in an entertaining way. You can use little illustrations that will give as good an understanding as a complete mechanical drawing. But some technical reports are so dry and dusty that if you put a pile of them in a hydraulic press and apply millions of pounds pressure to it, not a drop of juice will run out.

I stopped in a bookstore today, and the manager said, "I have a new book on thermodynamics. I think you'd be interested in it."

"I'd like to look at it," I replied. "I don't think it would be interesting though."

So he showed me the book, and there were about seventeen pages of differential equations on the second law of thermodynamics. Now you haven't any idea how integrated into our whole social life is this second law of thermodynamics. And, after a look at those equations, I was even more astonished.

But we have analyzed this and squeezed it down, and here is what we find that the second law of thermodynamics says: "You can't push on something that is going faster than you are." It is more complicated than that, of course, and they say it in very elegant language. They say that heat by itself cannot transfer itself from a lower level to a higher level. But that is the same thing.

What we need is a general education in simplification—telling things in a simple way. Personally, I believe you can simplify anything you understand. One fellow calls a thing by one name and another by a different name.

Here is a clock running. We go into the physics department and we learn the vibration of the pendulum and we write it down on our cuffs while we take the final examination. We go into the vibration of a string of a musical instrument and we learn the formula for that. Then we go into the electrical engineering department and we learn about the conditions for resonance in electric circuits. We go into radio, into X-ray and all that.

We get a lot of equations, entirely different ones, but they are all the same thing. They are only the expressions of the relationships that exist where you have both mass and elasticity. Wherever you have those two factors of mass and elasticity you are going to get a vibratory condition. But a fellow comes out with nine special cases. He is all crammed full of formulas, but he does not have the slightest comprehension of the general principle.

This field of communication is one in which people sometimes fail to understand even simple words. I once used this story in a speech to oil men in Texas. There was an oil man who was quite sick. He went to several medical specialists and they all told him: "Now you can't live very long. Better get your affairs in shape, because you're likely to drop off just like that."

But he had been in college with a fellow who was now a country doctor, and he went to see him. This doctor put him in the little hospital there and after a few days of observation and treatment reported, "Joe, I think there has been a mistake in the diagnosis of your case. You're all right. Go back home and go to work."

"Well, Doc, that's wonderful! How much do I owe you?"

"With the hospital and everything, it comes to about a thousand dollars," said the doctor.

"Oh, no, that's not enough. You saved my life. Isn't there anything in the world you'd like to have?"

"Well, yes," said the doctor, "I'd like to have a set of matched golf clubs."

"I'll get them for you," promised the grateful oil man.

The doctor didn't hear anything from him for months. Then one evening the oil man called up and said: "Hello, Doc. Gosh, I've surely had a time getting those golf clubs for you. I've got eight of them, but they're not too well matched. Two of them haven't got swimming pools."

Engineers have been told by many intelligent people that it is the mechanization of the country that has caused its difficulties. We are criticized also for being materialists. They say that we've lost the other phases of life. Our spiritual side has been sacrificed.

I want to tell you a little story which I think is as good an answer to that as anything I know. A good many years ago I went down to Yucatan. At that time they had twenty-five miles of highway, from Progreso to Merida, which is the capital. They had about fifty automobiles in the nation. Some twenty years later when we went back to Yucatan they had hundreds of miles of roads and ten or fifteen thousand automobiles, a great many trucks, and much of the farming was being done with tractors.

On our first trip we had gone down to the Mayan ruins at

Chichen Itza and it had taken us a whole day to get there, starting at four o'clock in the morning. This time we could drive to Chichen Itza in an hour and a half or two hours. They have meanwhile developed that place into beautiful parks and scenic spots.

One member of our party said, "I'd like to talk to one of the people who live here, one of these native Mayans." So the driver of one of our cars said: "If you don't mind going down this little side road, we can talk to my aunt. I know she won't object to your coming in."

So we went and talked to her. She couldn't speak English but our driver was a good interpreter. Here was a woman who had never had a pair of shoes, but had raised a family.

She had three prized possessions. One was an old Singer sewing machine that she had used to make the simple clothing for her family. She had an old phonograph and some records. But the new thing she had was a radio given to her by her son, who drove a bus between Merida and Chichen Itza.

She said to us: "I am no longer a lonely person in the jungles of Yucatan. I am a citizen of the world. I get the music, I get the news. I am a citizen of the world."

And all of that was produced by simple material arranged by engineers. Do you think we have done anything to the spiritual activity of that woman? Do you think that in any sense of the word doing so was materialistic only? We're doing that all over the world today by the industrial know-how of our country. And I keep wondering how we can tell our own people what we are and how we do these things. But take it from an old engineer—making your country's progress your profession is an exciting and rewarding way to spend your life.

I AM FOR THE DOUBLE-PROFIT SYSTEM

As an engineer and man of science, Kettering professed to know nothing about business. Yet he organized more than one company to make and market new products which he developed, and these became very successful. To save a Dayton bank from collapse, he became a banker also, and soon made it the principal banking institution in the city.

In Kettering's speeches he put forth many progressive concepts of business. And, considering the early time when some of them were spoken, they were all the more progressive.

I DON'T KNOW ANYTHING ABOUT BUSINESS. BUT I KNOW THIS: If you have a product that somebody wants, and they are willing to pay you more for it than it costs you to make it, you don't have to bother about the bankers too much. But I also know that if the customer doesn't think the article is worth considerably more to him than he paid for it you won't sell him another one.

This is what I call the double-profit system—a reasonable profit for the maker and a much greater profit for the customer. The customer's profit is the value of something, such as the telephone, electric lights, or an automobile, over and above what he had to pay for it. It is that how-much-more-he-would-be-willing-to-pay which measures the customer's profit. And often it is a lot more than the manufacturer gets for the article.

In discussing this with a friend of mine, who is in the machinery business, he said that for their particular line (which is centrifugal separators) the customer, as a rule, made twenty-five times as much profit by the use of the machine as the manufacturer did for designing, building, and selling it. In other cases there is an even better ratio to the customer—and to the ultimate consumer, the public.

Of course, if the manufacturer does not make a profit the sheriff gets him. Two people govern the lives of all industry, the customer

135

on the one side and the sheriff on the other, and you have to steer in between. The difference between the manufacturer's cost and selling price goes under what to some people is the nasty name of "profit." But you see how much worse it is not to make a profit.

So we talk about the small profit of the manufacturer and miss the great thing that built the cities, that built the highways, that built the railroads, which was the plus of the profit of utility over actual cost. It is the customer's profit that has built this country. It wasn't built from manufacturing profits. If you want to make market surveys, find out what the customer's profit on the article is going to be, and that will tell you whether it will go or not.

The customer also determines, in large measure, the design of a product. I can remember, years ago, that the first automobiles had whipsockets and rein guards. The cars didn't look right without them and people wouldn't buy if they weren't there.

There is an interesting story along this line about the incandescent electric lamp. As many will remember, the old lamp bulb had a tip on it. This was a relic of the connection used to create the vacuum in the bulb. Later, a way was found to hide that connection in the socket end. You would think that an improvement like that would be accepted readily by the public, but it was not. People refused to buy bulbs without the tip. So for years, even though the tip served no actual purpose, it continued to appear on the end of the light bulb. It was made smaller and smaller each year, though, until finally it was washed out. While it lasted, it was known as the psychological tip.

A good purchase by anybody is one in which he thinks he got his money's worth, for values depend upon what you think of things. If you pay ten dollars in New York to go to a show and when it is over you say, "I am glad I went to that show," that is a good investment. If you paid only fifty cents and didn't like the show, it was no good. It depends altogether upon whether the purchase meets your desires or not.

A very interesting thing that some economists may not understand is the fact that the minute you fabricate a thing it belongs to the public and not to you. The reason you have to reduce prices during overproduction is that the public doesn't want your product. The public knows that what you have made you cannot refabricate, and they take it at just whatever price they please. It belongs to them anyhow. You are just holding it in trust.

If you have a ton of raw ore, you can do anything you want with it. It belongs to you. But when you roll it into one-inch bar stock, you don't have anything to say about it from then on. So you had better study the stock sizes far enough in advance so that you will roll the right size.

We have followed for so long the bankers' definition of prosperity —bank balances and bank clearances—that people don't have quite the true picture of what constitutes prosperity. Let me give you an engineer's definition of it: Prosperity is the tonnage of useful materials moving through the channels of trade. We have been talking dollars so long that we have not quite grasped that what we work with and work for are materials and goods.[1] A dollar isn't anything but a receipt for service performed.

The clearinghouse of the bank is the negative side of the cycle. It is the negative wire, so to speak, of the great electric current of prosperity. And we have concentrated so much on the negative wire that we forget about the positive current, which is the flow of useful materials through the channels of trade.

Nobody wants anything new, because it disturbs the old things. You have your card indexes all made up, and if you bring in a new thing that means you have to write them all over and somebody figures out how much that will cost, and it isn't worth it, he says. But the change that brings about the inception of a new thing is small at its beginning. It is so trivial, the thing that swings the balance one way or the other!

It may be illustrated in this way. If you get on a train at Cleveland you can buy a ticket either for New York or Boston. You can eat in the same dining car and sit in the same club car

---

[1] Said in 1928 at the First New England Research Conference.

until you get to Albany. And there the train parts. They throw a little triangular piece of iron and the car that is going to Boston deviates from the track of the one going to New York, at the beginning by only a few thousandths of an inch. But the net result is that one goes to Boston and the other to New York. At the time the change is made, though, it didn't look as though it was worth while doing. Yet it may be the deviation point which throws a thing over here or over there.

A good many years ago we realized that the closed automobile body was going to be an important factor in our industry. It was taking two weeks or more to finish a car body. And, when some thousands of bodies were going to be built every day, you would have to have an awfully big paint shop. In fact, if you had that many bodies in process, you would never get any of them out, because in moving them around many would be scratched and have to be refinished.

So I set out to see whether we couldn't reduce the time it was taking to finish an automobile body. Well, naturally, what you do in such a case is to call in the experts. That is the first thing to do, but the last to pay any attention to. Any time you want to stop anything just call a conference. They all vote that you can't do it.

Anyway, I sent for some paint makers, some painters, and some paint chemists. I put the problem before them, saying, "You are using the same old kind of finish on automobiles that you used to put on pianos. You know what would happen if you were to set your piano out in the middle of the back yard and let it get rained on and let the sun beat down on it while it was still wet. The neighbors would take you out to the insane asylum. Why can't we get paints that will stand up better? And why can't we get paints that we can put on more rapidly?"

They finally agreed that the finishing time of more than two weeks might possibly be cut a day or two.

"That isn't good enough," I said.

"How long do you think it ought to take to paint an automobile body?" they asked.

Well, to get the problem really in front of them, I said, "About an hour."

"Why, man," they exclaimed, "don't you know you can't finish an automobile body in an hour?"

"No, I don't know that," I replied. "Why can't you?"

"Because the paint won't dry."

"Can't you do something to make it dry faster?"

"Not a thing in the world," they said. "Nature fixes that."

A little later in New York I saw in the window of a jewelry store some pin trays finished in a new kind of lacquer. I went in and bought a 75-cent tray for the usual New York price of $12.50. From the maker of the tray I found that the finish was made by a fellow over in New Jersey.

I went over there and found a little laboratory in back of a business block. I said to the fellow who was running it, "I would like to buy a quart of that lacquer."

He said, "My goodness, I never made a quart of it before. What do you want to do with it?"

"I want to finish an automobile door," I told him.

"You can never do it in the world," he said.

"Why not?"

"It dries too fast," he said. "If you put it in one of your spray guns it will dry and blow away before it reaches the door."

"Can't you do anything to slow it down?" I asked.

"Not a thing," he said.

There I had the two extremes. It took two and a half years of intensive experimentation, conducted cooperatively between our men and those in the du Pont Company, to get a finish halfway between the paint that couldn't be speeded up and the paint that couldn't be slowed down. But we finally succeeded in getting a fast-drying finish which had the qualities necessary for application to automobile bodies. The change gave us also a finish far better than that we started out with.

Shortly after that new finish had been successfully established I was visited in my office by one of the paint men present at that first conference. I happened to have an ordinary paint color card lying on my desk and I said to him—he had driven there in his automobile—"If you were having your car refinished, what color would you have it done in?" After deliberating and thinking whether his wife would like it or not, he picked out a certain color and we went to lunch. When we came back we sat around and talked for a little while. Finally he said, "I'll have to be going."

He then looked out the window and exclaimed, "My car is gone!"

"No, it isn't," I said. "That's your car out there. Didn't you tell me that was the color you would like? We just refinished your car while you were at lunch."

I have said before that self-satisfaction is one of the world's worst diseases. And that is especially so in business. Maybe you remember the Pierce-Arrow automobile company in Buffalo years ago. It was a pretty fine company and was putting out an equally fine car. In fact, the car they were making was so good that when a customer survey was made it showed that about 98 per cent of the owners of Pierce-Arrows were so satisfied that they agreed that the next car they would buy would be another Pierce-Arrow. So those Pierce-Arrow engineers got the idea that they had made the best car there was and there was no use going any further. Well, the company went out of business. That very satisfaction made them stand still.

The point I am making is that nothing is going to stand still. So when you have customers who are too satisfied, you want to be scared. You had better get some of them dissatisfied. The advertising fellows chide us about that because they say a satisfied customer is the greatest advertisement we have got. I think it is fine for the customer to be satisfied so far as the product is concerned, but I don't want him to be so satisfied that he does not hope to get something still better and that he will get more for his money the next time he buys. And I want to have that better thing ready for him when that time comes.

I was at one time chief engineer of the National Cash Register

Company. Up to that time a large portion of the business of the company had been in furnishing cash registers to bars. But cash registers did not wear out fast and the bar business had reached near saturation.

We had other types of registers which were more expensive and which gave a great deal more information. But, because of the inconvenience of operating those registers, in which a hand crank had to be turned around twice for each sale, they were not practical for bar work.

What we did was to develop an electric drive for our better register, thereby making it as easy to operate as the so-called press-down key registers then being used almost universally in bars. This improvement opened wide that market for cash registers. It did so not because the old registers were worn out but because we were able to give those customers a new thing which to them was more than worth the difference in price.

We have to indoctrinate ourselves with the belief that no article should be kept off the scrap pile longer than it takes to provide a better article. Obsolescence is not a dangerous thing. It is an economy. Prosperity and obsolescence are tied together, and obsolescence makes prosperity. I don't believe that you can ever expect to have a high degree of employment in a country where there are not enough new things coming along to obsolete the old before they are written off on the depreciation account.

This is not waste; waste comes when we cling too long to the old things. Of course, technological development must bring not the little 1 or 2 per cent advance, but something in which the advantage of the new thing is more than the unused value of the old thing. If you can't do that, you can't use obsolescence.

We have lots of things that we ought to tear down and throw away. The first thing you know, the banker and economist say, "Where are you going to get the money from?" I am not worried about where we are going to get the money. Where did we get the money to build New York City? We dug it out of the ground. All that money is is the barter checks for man-hours and pounds of material that have been converted into useful things for mankind. There is a lot of rock in New York State yet. You can build another New York. But somebody has to have it in mind, and it has got to be of use to people.

To me the thing we call prosperity is brought about by people wanting something they haven't got. If a man asks you for a raise, it is not because he wants more money. It is because he wants to take that money and buy something with it, some material thing. When he buys that something, somebody has to work; and, when that somebody has to work, he buys something too. So in turn this obsolescence factor is a measure of human activity.

What we have done is to produce on a necessity basis. But progress is made on the want basis. In 1930 I was talking to a member of the English Parliament about the dole situation over there. I said, "I can fix all that." And he said, "What can you do?"

I told him that I would get some advertising man to advertise radios, phonographs, pianos, and all the things you don't need. The first thing you know somebody would buy them. Then somebody would have to make them and employ some people, and soon you would have everybody working. I felt as though I had saved the country, you know, when the man said to me, "My word, who'd buy one of those things anyhow?"

The minute you begin to create new wants, which are entirely different from needs then you begin to get a mental reaction which is of far more importance than the economic reaction. People begin to want things that they do not need and, as they begin to want those things, they become more alert mentally, more willing to work, more willing to do the unusual thing. Consequently, we break the routine of that civilization and step it up to an entirely new thing.

The automobile has entered into that situation and has created a new kind of want which we believe now [2] has developed into a need. That early term, "pleasure car," has been abandoned. The automobile is contemporaneous with the motion picture, the radio, and

[2] In 1928.

all of those things which nobody needed at all, but which would be missed and make this a dull place to live in if we didn't have them.

The minute you create those wants, things that you would like to have, it becomes monotonous without them. Then you have started a preliminary type of industry which will develop rapidly in a generation or two into a fundamental need. You can get along without any of these things, but you are less happy than if you have them.

During the 1930's a good friend of mine from England, Sir Josiah Stamp, later Lord Stamp, chief economist of the Bank of England, made a number of talks in this country on the necessity of limiting inventions. He called it "the birth control of inventions." His arguments were based entirely on the idea that you could not have a stable economic world if it was going to be continually upset, as he put it, by the introduction of new inventions. He contended that our modern methods of research and development were going to be detrimental in the long-range economic development of the whole world, as science was moving faster than social and political adjustments could follow.

That reasoning looked bad for my business as a developer of new products. So I answered it. I tried to show that, on the contrary, inventors don't invent enough. We are told by the most reliable information you can get, from statistics, that there is something like forty billions of dollars idle in our American banks. We are also told that there are something between five and ten millions of people out of employment.[3] The number out of employment is dependent upon which party you belong to. Nevertheless, there is an unemployment problem.

Now the reason we have that, I said, is because those two things are opposite ends of the same stock. I think it is because we are too far behind in our development and I think the measure of how far behind we are is represented by the forty billions of dollars out

[3] This was said during the depression years of the 1930's.

of employment and the five or ten million people out of work.

We have many people who are talking about dividing up what we have. But we don't want to study division. We want to study multiplication.[4] Give research a chance in this country and it will start the wheels. If we had new products, new projects, new reconstructive types of industry, we would have our money employed and we would also have our people at work.

During World War II, which came just a few years after my debate with Lord Stamp, another prominent Englishman made this statement: "I think we wouldn't have won the Battle of Britain without 100-octane gasoline." That was said by Geoffrey Lloyd, Great Britain's wartime Petroleum Secretary, and 100-octane gasoline was an important invention, if ever there was one, or rather it was a whole series of inventions.

The last time I saw Lord Stamp was in England in 1938. I had just returned to England from Germany; and, knowing that over there they were getting ready to go to war, I asked Lord Stamp whether or not England felt prepared to meet it. He replied that it was not necessary that England be prepared for war, because Germany could not fight a long war. In support of his view, he pulled out a piece of paper and set up the relative percentages of Germany's gold reserve and various other indexes which are commonly used in rating a nation's commercial ability or industrial activity. He said that, with Germany's indexes so low, she would go broke before she could even start an important war.

This opinion of his proved to be a great fallacy, of course. And it was unfortunate that Lord Stamp and his Lady were killed by a German bomb which fell at their home outside London during the Battle of Britain. I should like to have been able to discuss this subject with him further. But I'm not sure whether economists and inventors will get to the same place when they die.

In engineering it is a fundamental that there is no such thing as perpetual motion. But for many years men did try for perpetual motion, and somehow it just pretty nearly worked, but not quite.

[4] Said in 1935 in address to American Association of Advertising Agencies.

We almost got the engine to run the generator, to make the current, to put into the boiler, to make the steam to run the engine. But it didn't quite work out.

Still, we sometimes don't recognize that perpetual motion is merely a superficial way of trying to get something for nothing. So we have today many social and economic perpetual motion schemes which haven't been recognized as such. But economic perpetual motion will wash out just as surely as mechanical and we will find that we have to produce things in order to have them.

One danger in this country is failure to determine the difference between progressive thinking and false promises. The false promise fellow uses exactly the spirit of the progressive thinkers to misrepresent his promise still further. He says, "Nobody thought anything of the Wright brothers when they flew, so why do you say I am off the beam?"

Some men in industry and finance suffer from a serious deficiency in imagination. I've often wished that we had an imagination serum that might be injected into some such persons. Think what it would mean to the country if we could take our financial leaders and infect them with this vision-virus and find them suddenly expanded mentally and spiritually, men with the imagination so badly needed. To the unimaginative the world is always finished.

Some other people keep zoos, and those zoos are what I call pet prejudices. I said once to a group of fairly high-salaried men, "I am going to recommend that the company keep you on the payroll at your regular salary on just one condition. That condition is that you never get nearer to the research laboratories than one mile. Because if you do it will cost us a couple of million dollars to feed your pet prejudices, and we don't want any zoos here."

In the many years I have been in industry I have designed a lot of machines. Some thirty-five years after I had made a certain development I was told that it had now been adopted in all the models being made. So I said, "Now, wait a minute. Who died?"

The answer was that nobody had died, but that Tom had retired.

Now Tom, a high executive there, was getting about $50,000 a year. So I figured that if they had paid him $500,000 a year to stay away from the plant they would still have saved a million dollars a year. I think that every once in a while we ought to analyze ourselves to find out how much more we may be worth to the company by staying away than by coming to work.

In business the one fellow you never think much about, whom you don't know, sits back and controls the whole thing, and that fellow is your customer. He is the final inspector. Instead of trying to regiment people into what you like or what you don't like, you try instead to give them what they want.

I have often said that all of the profit and loss on any manufacturer's books are the applause and the hisses of the customers. If it is black it is applause and if red it is hisses. I am willing to be inconvenienced with my customer, and I don't try to govern what he wants. If he wants me to turn the article upside down, he is going to get it that way. He is paying for it, and if he likes the show it's all right with me. Remember that you and I get no place in the world except in proportion as we serve the fellow who pays for our dinner.

I have said that war is economics in reverse. In peacetime, the purpose of business is to make a desirable article, sell it at an attractive price, deliver it at a definite time, and try to render a worth-while service to the customer. That is normal business. In war however, you try to make something the "customer" does not want, try to deliver it to him when he least expects it or when it will do him the most possible harm, and otherwise try to make things as costly or as unpleasant for him as you can.

Have you any really legitimate reason—if that necktie you have on wasn't given to you—why you bought that kind of tie? You must have gone into the store and looked at it and said, "I like that one," and picked it out. Now, did you analyze why you picked it out or why you liked it? You don't have to do that. Nobody has to say *why* he does or does not like a thing. That is a part of his predetermined and unregimented character—about the only one, too.

So what about the profit motive? Is there any substitute for it as a vital force in stimulating progress? Although, in actual fact, I think it should be called the profit-and-loss motive. So long as we recognize that industry has been built primarily because of the service it rendered to the people who got the product, and so long as we think in terms of giving the customer what he wants, not what we may want, then we can go ahead. If we do that and at the same time make sure that the customer's profits are good, we don't need to worry about anything else.

MASS PRODUCTION

Kettering thought that mass production, the key to which is the precise duplication of parts, is so important to people that in his speeches he often talked about it. In his view, the importance of mass production is its marvelous effectiveness in expanding the production and lowering the cost of things. To help more people understand this, he also wrote in 1947, with Allen Orth, a small book entitled, American Battle for Abundance, A Story of Mass Production.

YOU HAVE HEARD A LOT ABOUT MASS PRODUCTION. BUT MASS production is perhaps less understood and more misinterpreted than anything else in the world, largely because some of our magazine writers have seen an assembly line. Now the assembly line has no more to do with mass production than the folding machine at the end of the great printing press has to do with the printing business.

The thing that we have developed in this country, beyond other manufacturing countries, is the ability to make duplicate or interchangeable parts. If you tear down a piece of apparatus into its parts, and make more parts just like them, you can put the parts together again and have more of the apparatus. The parts cannot be put together to make anything else.

There is a story about a man in Germany before World War II who stole parts from the factory where he worked, which he supposed was making baby carriages. "You know I tried to steal the parts to make one of those buggies," he said, "and when I put it together it turned out to be a machine gun." He said that he couldn't put the parts together in any way so that it would come out a baby carriage. Mass production is just that simple—the duplication of parts.

The machine gun is a good illustration of the point I am trying to make. I happened to be in Dayton during World War II when government representatives came to one of our companies there with a 50-caliber machine gun which they asked that concern to manufacture. Well, that company, which produced refrigerators, had never made any guns. So, right away they said, "We don't know anything about the gun business."

But I said to them, "That is a good thing. You don't need to know anything about the gun business, because you are not going into the gun business. The man who designed this gun and proved it out is the one who is in the gun business. All he is asking you to do is to make some more pieces exactly like these."

I said to the colonel who brought the machine gun in, "Will this gun shoot the way you want it to?"

"Yes," he replied, "this gun has been through all the firing tests and is OK."

"That's all we need to know," I said. "If you have drawings of the parts of that gun, all we need to do is make parts exactly like those in the drawings, and *what can it do but shoot when we put it together?*" Of course, if you haven't got a gun that will shoot, then you have nothing to start with. In other words, you have to have copy before you go to press.

As a matter of fact, the people who first started mass production or interchangeability, or whatever you want to call it, were the printers. More than five hundred years ago Gutenberg developed the art of printing, and to him goes the credit for the first step in the mass-production idea. The whole art of printing is simply a matter of making something just like something else. A man writes something; it is checked and edited. Then it is set in type, and every time the press goes around we get another copy. Of course, that is limited application of the principle of duplication, since printing is done in only two dimensions, whereas mechanical devices or moving mechanisms require for successful operation accurate workmanship in three dimensions.

I once had lunch with William S. Knudsen who had as his guest an eminent author from abroad. The guest talked much about how the so-called standardized conditions under which we Americans live and work would drive him crazy. "You all wear the same kind of clothes," he said, "drive the same kind of cars, and do the same things over and over again. Sometimes I do my writing with a pen, sometimes with a pencil. And now and again I want to have a change and just smoke my pipe or go for a stroll."

"Then I suppose it annoys you," I said, "that when your books are published, all the copies are just alike."

"Oh, no," he replied, "They are supposed to be that way."

"The man who publishes your books doesn't care how you write," I said. "He simply takes your manuscript, sets it up in type and prints it. There your individuality ends, for the printer makes all the copies alike. Well, that is just what we do here in Detroit. We publish automobiles. We print them on punch presses and gather and bind them on assembly lines.

"Just as in your case as a writer, the individuality and ingenuity are put into the automobile and other products in the research, the designing, the styling, the testing and all the other long preparations for that final process. It is those preparation phases which are the equivalents of your pencil or pen writing and your strolling and pipe smoking."

Although this idea of exact duplication became firmly established in printing, it was a long time before people seemed to have thought of applying it to anything else. About the first instance of historical record was the attempt of Louis XIV to clothe his army in uniforms. Louis XIV wanted all his 100,000 soldiers to wear the same kind of suits, made out of the same kind of cloth and all trimmed alike. This became one of the first mass production jobs.

No one seemed to have thought of applying it to anything else— that is, until Eli Whitney came on the scene. Every American knows the story of Whitney's invention of the cotton gin and what that has meant to the textile industry. However, few are as familiar with his later development.

It came about this way: In 1798, our government was in great need of rifles. It was then that Eli Whitney suggested the idea that has completely changed American industry. He offered to make 10,000 rifles for the government in two years—a number which seems small to us now when we can produce that many in a day. But at that time production in such volume was unprecedented.

Whitney's plan was to build a set of special tools with which to make each part of the gun. These parts were to be very accurate. As Whitney put it, they were to be "as much alike as the successive impressions of a copperplate engraving." By using this system, he would duplicate each piece of the very best gun available.

By the end of the first year he had produced only 500 acceptable guns. His contract called for 4,000 by that time, and he was still designing machinery. The War Department and Congress became very impatient. So Whitney packed up the parts of ten guns—triggers, barrels, stocks, etc.—and went to Washington. On arriving at the Capitol, he placed a table in the conference room and on it laid piles of each one of these parts. He asked the officials to take one part *at random* from each pile. Then he proceeded to assemble those into a finished musket—no filing, no machining—the parts fitted perfectly.

Whitney had to face that criticism before he could complete the operation, because nobody appreciated the necessity for make-ready time. You may recall that in industry we had the same trouble during World War II. The newspapers said, if industry can make 20,000 automobiles a day, why can't they produce "X" tanks the next day? They didn't realize that, unlike the printer, we had to set up an entirely different kind of type. You can't *print* tanks with the same type that you use to *print* automobiles.

At the time of Pearl Harbor, our enemies thought they had caught us completely unprepared. They knew we had great factories turning out millions of so-called luxury items such as automobiles, refrigerators, and radios. But they reasoned that this in itself was in their favor because they were sure our complex production machine could not be converted in time for us to compete with their amassed inventory of tanks and airplanes.

But they underestimated our not so secret "secret weapon." This was the great flexibility and capacity of American industry, coupled with our production "know-how," which had resulted from our system of making yearly model changes. Thousands of American engineers and production men had accustomed themselves down through the years to yearly reconversion of their designs and production setups. And, what was more important in a War of Horsepower, we were accustomed to turning out some 200 million horsepower of gasoline engines annually!

If we are going to duplicate parts, we have to set up a most rigid system of machining and inspection in order to have all of the parts come out exactly right. So the whole system of interchangeable manufacture is based upon our ability to make accurate measurements. In the early days of mechanics a shaft was measured with an ordinary pair of calipers. The mechanic who could guess most closely had something uncanny about him. He had a delicacy of touch that no one understood.

Then came the micrometer with which a man could measure a thousandth part of an inch. But later after the Johansson blocks were devised by the Swedish engineer, Carl Johansson, a person, using the indicating gauge, could very easily measure with accuracies that went to the hundred thousandth part of an inch. Of the thousands of pieces that enter into automobile construction, for instance, many, such as ball or roller bearings are accurate within a hundred thousandth of an inch.

The first automobiles were nearly all hand-built, and in those early days "handmade" was a mark of excellence. Many thought foreign workmanship superior to American, and would not buy an automobile unless it had been made abroad. In that period, the Royal Automobile Club of London awarded each year the Dewar Trophy for the greatest advance made by any motorcar during the year. And in 1906, Cadillac, an early leader in precision manufacture, decided to try for this trophy on the basis of interchangeability of parts and shipped three cars to London.

After being tested the cars were taken apart and the parts all put in one large pile. American mechanics, with ordinary hand tools, assembled three complete automobiles from that mixture of parts. Afterwards, the three cars passed the prescribed operation test perfectly, and for the first time an American company was awarded the Dewar Trophy.

The techniques of mass production have accelerated the invention and design of thousands of new products and provided work for millions of people, and at much higher wages than would have been possible otherwise. Our great skill in making special tools and gauges, coupled with the progressive system of assembly, makes it possible to produce practically any type of mechanism in large quantities.

Thus the tremendous strides made in improving standards of measurement guaranteed the success of the mass production system pioneered by Eli Whitney. And this system of mechanical duplication—or mass production, as it is called—is vital to our progress and prosperity. We have 6 per cent of the land of the earth. We have 7 per cent of the population. But we have so disproportionately greater percentages of all things that we regard as essential to modern living that it is perfectly amazing.

Now it isn't important that we have these things, but the matter that is important is how did we come to have them? Why is it that we have 90 per cent of all the television sets, about 70 per cent of all the automobiles, almost 70 per cent of all the telephones in the world—and all the way down the line? We have discussed this many, many times and we ought to be able to say it in a few words. It is the concensus of a lot of the scientific people and industrial people that we have in this country two things that nobody else in the world has had. First, we have had a higher degree of individual freedom, and second, we have had a greater use of tools. And those tools are very important.[1]

Many substitutes for our American system have been and are

---

[1] Said in 1951 before the advances in other nations as an aftermath of World War II.

being suggested, but to date none of them has *proved* itself capable of producing standards of living comparable to ours. It is a time-tried, proved process for producing more and better things for everyone. It is tangible evidence that the dreams and efforts of hundreds of pioneers were not fruitless. Our democratic system permitted these men to work out things for themselves in their own way. And today, as a result, we can enjoy and pass on to our children the highest standards of living ever known to man.

WHAT IS THE AUTOMOBILE BUSINESS?

As one who spent about forty active years in the automobile industry and who contributed to it many advances, Kettering spoke often and with intimate knowledge about it. He served the industry first as an independent inventor and afterwards for twenty-seven years as head of research for General Motors Corporation.

Among the most outstanding of his many contributions, to name just two, were the electric self-starter and the improvement in fuel economy which came by locating and clearing the rock-strewn paths to knock-free gasoline and to high compression in engines. In the accomplishment of the latter Kettering was not alone at all but, through his early and extended researches and through his articulate and persistent push for progress in the field, he was the principal pioneer.

WHAT IS THE AUTOMOBILE BUSINESS? IT ISN'T MERELY THE manufacturing of motorcars. That is a very small part of it. Nearly all business has some connection with the automobile business. It is the building of highways; it is the gasoline station, the petroleum industry, the rubber industry, the making of steel and glass, the operation of trucks, buses, and taxicabs. It is even the real estate business, and the hot dog stand. It has made deep changes in how people travel, how farmers grow and market crops, and where schools are built.

For every man employed in the automobile factories there are ten employed outside. So many other activities are a part of the motorcar industry that today one person in every seven is earning his living in the highway transport industries. In fact, there is hardly a man in the nation whose capacity to earn a living would not be at least partially blighted if the automobile industry were by some evil wizardry shrunk to its status as of fifty years ago.

The development of individual transportation is perhaps one of the most spectacular things in the life of man. We have always been people who wanted to go places. Some wise man once said that the reason we need so much transportation is that nothing is where you can use it and nobody is where he wants to be.

The automobile has grown from humble beginnings to a world-wide industry. I knew the automobile industry when it was a baby industry. I knew it when cars were sneered at as buggyauts and electrobats; when they were commonly regarded as jokes.

I remember my first automobile trip. We went from Dayton to Springfield, Ohio.[1] We left Dayton at nine o'clock in the morning and got back at eleven o'clock that night, and we had spent nearly all that time on the road. People said: "Why, you could have driven over there with a horse and buggy in that time!" Of course we could, but we wouldn't have been half as dirty or had half as much fun.

Pioneering in a barn-loft laboratory in Dayton, we developed and installed on the 1912 Cadillac the first successful electric self-starter. In the years since, I have had my share of excitement in seeing the industry zoom up and up. More than 99 per cent of the 150 million automobiles made so far have been made since I came into the business.[2]

But suppose the automobile and all it has brought were suddenly subtracted from our life. Our cities would have to shrink back within their limits of fifty years ago. Thousands of small towns would be cut off from the world except for a train or two a day. Tens of thousands of villages would be hidden beyond the barrier of bad roads.

The greatest factor that has to do with the stagnation of the human mind is that of monotony, for monotony is a horrible thing. And the monotony factor has been broken much more by the automobile than perhaps anything that has ever come. The telephone has come into nearly every farmer's house, the automobile has come into practically every farmer's yard, and with these came

---

[1] Distance, 25 miles.
[2] Said in 1955.

the ability to hear and the ability to go at will. Thus the country dweller has changed his entire perspective in life.

I sometimes think that we forget how great a transportation system our automobiles have become. We have roughly 60 million motor vehicles in the United States,[3] and if we take five passengers per automobile, that is 300 million seats. We have in the United States only about 160 million population, which means that if we took every man, woman and child for a ride at the same time, we would have 140 million seats left over. And that would be enough for us to take along at the same time all the people in England, France, and Italy.

Who would want to go back to the days before the automobile? It is a necessity to many people, in some instances even more than that. I recall a humorous story of a man who had been having his troubles with the depression in the 1930's. He was recounting his woes to a friend.

"I lost my job," he said, "and went home to my father's to live. My wife went to her family's. We sent the children to the orphan asylum. I shot my dog. If things get much worse, I'll have to give up my car."

But when the first automobiles were built, nobody thought that they were the beginning of a new business, one that would cover the whole world, change the habits of people and their places of living—and incidentally give employment to millions. And if the men in this business had been content with those first cars, none of this would have come true. How many people today would pay two or three thousand dollars for a single-cylinder car, having a speed of 15 miles per hour, and without a top, electric lights, and other things which now make driving pleasant and convenient? How many people would want such a car at any price?

Yet I have in my files an advertisement, published in 1905 by the Winton Motor Carriage Company of Cleveland, Ohio. In it is a quotation from a letter written by Andrew Carnegie to Alexander

---

[3] Said in 1955.

Winton. Here in part is what Mr. Carnegie wrote: "We are greatly pleased with our new Winton. From the very start it has done its work and never failed us. There may be improvements yet to come in such autos, but it is difficult to see much room for them."

I've often said that the automobiles and other things we make are simply the packing cases by which we ship the skilled labor of the automobile manufacturer into the homes and the various other places for which the automobile is built. So also the radio that you buy at the store is simply a case in which is combined the skill and engineering of the people who designed and manufactured it.

There has been much discussion about whether the yearly model is the right thing or not. We think it is. We think that only by bringing together the accumulation of the year's work and putting it up on a new package can we really serve our customers properly. The automobile business is what it is today—a thriving industry, going day and night to keep up with demand—because it has followed a principle of continual improvement. I do not advocate change for the sake of change, nor do I say that a new thing is necessarily better because it is new or suddenly popular. Sometimes engineers improve things so they are not as good as they were. But if there is one thing the automobile has taught Americans in the last fifty years it is to expect constant improvement in the product.

Who buys the automobiles in your family—you? You just *pay* for them. Your wife and the kids buy the automobiles. That's who buys them. In other words, it is the younger generation that is the controlling factor. So long as we have younger generations we will have changes. Their views are new, their tastes are new, their likes are new—and emphatic. So the first law of economics is to be ready for a change.

I have been in this automobile business for many years. I have attended hundreds of sales conventions. I have eaten green turtle soup and salad with yellow dressing on it, and I have survived. I have heard these general sales managers get up and say, "This is

the most wonderful automobile that has ever been produced!"
You know, they have been right very year. And it can be true for
fifty years more, as long as we keep the idea of following the lead
of the public, as long as we keep trying to make things better and
to overcome the things we don't know.

I was present one time at an advertising meeting in which everybody was saying that as long as the company lasted they could
never make a better motorcar. That was contrary to my philosophy.
I was one of the speakers, one of the last speakers—they always
have the acrobats at the end. So I said: "Let's take this automobile
which you men have selected as being the highest form of automotive accomplishment, and let us seal it up in a glass case. It is
perfect, paint job perfect, upholstery perfect, engine perfect, transmission and everything. Let us get an expert sign painter to letter
inside that glass case, in gold letters like those on the front of
banks, the price of this automobile.

"Now we'll come back next year and take a look at the car. It
won't look so good then because there will be a new model out.
We can't get the posted price for it now, so we'll put the price of
two hundred dollars less on the glass case at the front. But this
time we'll print it there not in gold but in whitewash. We'll keep
on doing that each year. And what do you think we can get for
that car at the end of ten or fifteen years? It will be just as good
as it was when we put it in the case, but the only man who will
buy it is the junk dealer."

Why? Because the car depreciated? No, it is hermetically sealed
and couldn't depreciate. It is because, through the appreciation of
new car designs, the eyes on the outside looking through have
changed. That is what has changed. Values do not exist in material.
They exist in the minds of the people who are going to buy.

A man said to me the other day, "The trouble with you fellows
is that you are all the time changing your automobiles and
depreciating the old cars. You built and put on the market a good
automobile last year. This year you bring out a much improved
model. And by that improved model you depreciate the value of

the car that you sold last year. You depreciate it very much more than the mileage factor would indicate."

I said, "Why, no, we didn't depreciate the value of your old car at all. Did we scratch the paint of your car? Did we score a cylinder? Did we break a spark plug? No, we did not touch your car. It is hard to get a car touched even if you take it into a service department, let alone doing it maliciously. Your car is still just as good a piece of transportation as it was.

"So we did not depreciate your car at all. What we did do was to appreciate your mind. We have simply elevated your mental idea of what an automobile should be."

You all know the old, old question, which some of you probably have debated: "Which has contributed more to civilization, the pen or the sword?" We talk of the pen and the sword. But the great factor that has caused the wonderful development of all our civilizing devices has been the use of inanimate power. And I know of no piece of apparatus given to mankind that has entered into so many different ramifications of utility as has the gasoline engine.

It is hard to realize the importance of what the internal combustion engine has done. It is the first time man has ever had a small, mobile power unit that he could control and handle at will, and which is almost wholly reliable, as is evidenced by the large number of people who use it. It is a self-contained prime mover which doesn't require a licensed engineer. It is the farm tractor; it is the truck; it is the bus; it is the automobile. That small inanimate power device has made it possible for mankind to do, as he has never done before, the work of sustaining the human race.

Do we ever think what an inadequate, inefficient device the horse is from a power standpoint? The number of horsepower-hours that we got from a horse was small. We used him in the summertime, but we had to keep him warm all winter. Suppose a tractor had to be kept warm all winter. What should we say of the designer?

The automobile industry is the greatest power industry in the nation. If in a normal year we make five million cars, and if we rate them down to 50 horsepower—which is much below the advertised rating—that comes out 250 million horsepower of gasoline engines produced per year. And if we have 60 million cars out on the road that amounts—at the same discount on actual power rating—to a total of three billion horsepower. In all the central power stations in the United States there is only something like 150 million installed horsepower. So the horsepower in automobile engines amounts to 20 times or more that in all the central power stations in the nation.

For years those of us connected with the automobile industry thought that we were in a mechanical industry and that we were making machines. Then we came to realize that what we called a machine was only a piece of apparatus for the effective utilization of chemistry. After all, internal combustion is purely a chemical operation. We produce combustion of gasoline inside the cylinder, thereby making water and carbon dioxide, and with the resultant energy we ride around on the retort.

I have been interested for many years in the fuel that we use in automobiles. We talk about the tensile strength of steel being 150,000 pounds per square inch. I just computed what the "tensile strength" of gasoline is.

A gallon of gasoline, let us say, will run about ten miles.[4] Now, suppose you took this gallon of gasoline and drew it out into a thin wire 10 miles long. That is really what you do as you drive along. You stretch that gallon of gasoline out over 10 miles of road. And if you could measure it in this form you would find it to be about the size of a small pin. It would be about twenty-two thousandths of an inch in diameter. The pull of an automobile running at 60 miles an hour is about 500 pounds. So the tensile strength of that gasoline is about 1,500,000 pounds per square inch, and that is really the thing that pulls you along the road.

Engineers have long known that to increase the efficiency of

[4] Said in 1915.

internal combustion engines the compression ratio had to be increased. That is so because the tighter the charge is squeezed on the upstroke of the piston before ignition the farther the hot gases can expand on the downstroke after combustion, or the stronger and more sustained the push they can give. But attempts to use this important principle ran into fuel knock. Knock sets up a barrier to raising compression ratio, for it gets worse and worse as pressure is raised until it becomes destructive in violence.

In those early years nobody had any idea that the fuel was of very great importance. Nobody then questioned that gasoline wasn't the best that it could be. People spoke of the knock as carbon knock or spark knock and they said that engines had always knocked. That is their nature.

Many years ago in a very humble way I began research on knock in an effort to find how it might be overcome. We actually started that investigation in an old building that had been a tobacco warehouse. I read the first paper on results of that early study before the Society of Automotive Engineers in 1919. There I pointed out for the first time, I believe, that it is the molecular structure of a fuel which influences its behavior in combustion. And this was an entirely new point of view so far as either the petroleum industry or the automotive industry was concerned.

Later investigations in many places showed that the knocking characteristics of a fuel are related to the molecular structure in a very definite order. It was found that when carbons and hydrogens are hooked together as long chain molecules they knock badly, while a compact grouping of the same number of atoms is quite free from knock. This discovery—together with the development of tetraethyl lead, which meanwhile had been another important outcome of our research—has been utilized by the petroleum industry to make available higher and higher octane gasolines. This it has done through the discovery and application of new processes of refining which produce hydrocarbons of structures found to be good.

In 1938 I said this: "How far we can go with these improvements we do not know, but I am perfectly willing to make this as a prediction: You can't stop the rise in octane number until nature stops it for you. Here is one of the greatest steps in the world."

As gradually better and better gasolines became available, engines were designed to utilize them. Thus the common problem of providing increasingly better fuels for increasingly better engines has been a joint responsibility of the petroleum and automobile industries. A solution of the problem of knock in automobile engines would not have been possible without the hearty cooperation of both industries. Since this development began so many years ago, the octane number of automobile gasoline has risen from about 50 to about 100 and, over the same period, the compression ratios of automobile engines has been raised from about 4 to 1 to around 10 to 1.

From the first, it was recognized that the movement toward higher compression ratio in automobile engines could not be a rapid one. It could not be made all in one jump but had to be gradual and orderly because it required correlation between improvements in fuels and changes in engines. I was driving one time with an automobile test driver in the seat beside me, and he said, "Ket, maybe you had better change speed here." I asked, "Why so?"

"Well," he said, "there's a bridge out up ahead. You are going too fast to turn out but not quite fast enough to jump it."

To get high economy in engines you have to have high explosion pressures. There is no earthly way we know of to get high economy with low explosion pressures.

If you want to put a value on our long hard search, in which the entire oil industry cooperated, you can do so in three ways. First, the improved gasoline treated with tetraethyl lead made possible more efficient high compression engines, so that today two gallons of gasoline will do the work of three gallons of yesterday's fuel. Second, it permitted us each year to leave 25 million gallons of fuel in our underground reserves which otherwise would have been burned. And, third, at retail prices of gasoline, the American motorist has been saving 5 to 8 billion dollars a year.[5]

But we have not yet reached the limit of engine efficiency. As more developments are carried on by the automobile and petroleum industries, still further gains are possible. Why, we don't even know what makes an automobile run! It is so simple to explain it by saying that you take a charge of gasoline and air into the cylinder and compress it and ignite it with a spark, and it explodes and pushes the piston down, and that makes your car go.

If you stop right there, it is a logical explanation. But what does the spark do? What do you mean by combustion? We don't know why or how the spark sets off that explosion of gasoline and air. We have photographs that show that the spark jumps across the spark gap and is gone before the fire in the engine starts. It is not at all like starting a fire with a lighted match.

So I say, quite solemnly, that we haven't the slightest idea what really makes the contraption run. I just don't think we can live in the atmosphere of ignorance about what goes on there when our whole business depends upon it.

I have often said that the motorcar industry has been made possible by three factors: gasoline, alloy steels, and rubber. I always admired the man Dunlop, because I think that anybody who had the nerve to propose a rubber tire to run on the ground, when everybody knew that steel was the only thing that would do, must have been a man of distinct nerve and bravery. Dunlop planted the idea, and the simple rubber tube that he made progressed through various stages of evolution to the tire we have today.

The rubber industry has accomplished a miracle in the improvement of the tire. I have seen tires go from 3,000 miles to 75,000 or 80,000 miles. With the wonderful improvement in rubber, in cotton, in new fabrics today, we are getting surprisingly long

_____
[5] Said in 1958.

mileages.[6] As I said the other day in talking to a group of men, our tires today run almost as far as the advertising men say they do.

All of us remember when we thought it foolish to think of pneumatic tires for trucks. Yet all trucks are equipped with them today. The same is true of the tractor. In this latter instance pneumatic tires were not used to improve riding comfort but because tractors equipped with rubber tires take less power. I do not know what we can expect of tires in the future or how far we can expect the research to go. And, if we cannot predict the outcome of such a simple thing as a bag of wind—a tire full of air— it is foolish to attempt predictions of the future of anything so complicated as the motorcar.

But the conclusion reluctantly reached by a driver of one of the horse-drawn hansom cabs which stand at the 59th Street Plaza in New York is surely a sound one. He was talking to a fellow cabbie one day during the New York Automobile Show many years ago. The Plaza Hotel was crowded with automobile men and Fifth Avenue was full of motorcars. "Mr. Corrigan, I came to a different conclusion today," said the cabbie to one of his fellows.

"What is that?" asked Corrigan.

"I have come to the conclusion that the automobile is here to stay."

Put yourself back in the world of 1908, make a prediction of our world of 1958 and see how near you might have come to the facts—things such as radio, TV, and the new drugs. That is the reason when I am asked what great developments are likely to occur in the next fifty years I say frankly that I don't know, that they will be wonderful, and that they won't come out of textbooks. Neither do I know what the automobile of the future will look like, except that it will be what the people who buy it want it to be.

---

[6] Said in 1939.

A REVOLUTION ON THE RAILROAD

One of Kettering's major endeavors was the development of an improved diesel engine, an engine which played a vital part in transforming the powering of railroads by superseding the century-old steam locomotive. In different sizes, that engine found many other uses also—such as in marine service, in highway transport, and in powering a variety of industrial activities. But in this chapter Kettering speaks only about the diesel engine and the railroad.

WHENEVER WE DISCUSS ANYTHING THAT HAS TO DO WITH power and its development, we always have to consider the question of making a fire, because about 90 per cent of our power, with the exception of water power, is made by burning something. It is quite interesting to note that as you study the methods of making a fire, you are really studying the basic principles of the different types of engines manufactured today.

Bryant and May, the match manufacturers in England, have established a museum of fire making. If you should go through it I think you would be surprised to find what an enormous amount of work has been done on the simple problem of building fires.

There are three important ways of starting a fire: First, by friction. The boy scout does this by rubbing two pieces of wood together. The matchmakers in turn have built a simple device whereby you rub the head of a match over a box and a fire is started. That friction method is one of the oldest methods.

There is another method that was used by many tribes of aborigines, striking a spark off a flint. That is the same method that has now been glorified in your cigarette lighters, but with an artificial flint and a better type of combustible. The old flintlock gun was another type.

Spark ignition is the type we use in the automobile engine also. I sometimes think we forget how often we have to start the fires in a modern automobile engine. At 75 to 80 miles an hour we have to set about 250 to 300 fires per second. Starting one fire propels your car only about 6 inches and then you have to start another.

The third method of starting a fire, also quite old, was developed in the Far East, in Burma, Samoa, and similar places. It can be called compression ignition. The best way to illustrate it is to take an ordinary bicycle tire pump and crimp the hose so the air can't get out of it. If you take the plunger out of the pump and put a little dry moss or other combustible material in there, put the plunger back in, and push it down suddenly, the moss will take fire.

Now, this method has been used for centuries, and still is used, as a means of starting fires. That is because, when you compress air quickly, its temperature goes up. You have only to raise the temperature above the combustion point of the fuel and it will start to burn.

In some places in the tropics, I have seen people who have used the same little fire gun for thirty years lighting cigars and cigarettes. If you pull open one of those fire guns or fire syringes, you will see that it is nothing but an old-fashioned popgun, so to speak. You take out the piston and put in a little punk or something of that sort, replace the piston and push it in real hard, and you have a fire.

Now, these little fire guns are really the basis of the diesel engine. That is why I wanted to speak about them. What you do in a diesel engine is compress air quickly to a very high pressure, around six or seven hundred pounds and then inject the fuel. If you drew air from this room at normal temperatures and compressed it to six or seven hundred pounds the temperature would go up about six or seven hundred degrees Fahrenheit; and, if you then put fuel into it, it would ignite and burn.

That is what Rudolph Diesel did in making the diesel engine. His home was in Munich, Germany, and in the Deutsches Museum there he saw examples of the fire pistons I have mentioned. And he thought that that ought to be a good way to ignite the fuel in an internal combustion engine. This is how the diesel engine came to be conceived and the first one built about 1892. In Europe, and especially in England, they do not call it a diesel engine any more. They mention the two types of engines as spark ignition engines and compression ignition engines.

When toward the end of the last century Diesel developed his engine it naturally had to take the place of steam engines, because that was the only type of power-producing mechanism available or in use at that time. The new type of engine went into places where the slow-turning steam engine had been in use. This was especially true in ships where the propeller revolutions were in the neighborhood of one hundred per minute. This naturally forced the cylinders to be made large, which ran the weight of the engine up to one or two hundred pounds per horsepower. One of the descriptions that used to be applied to the diesel engine was that it was a mountain of cast iron with a rivulet of power. And that conception stood against it for a long while.

It was commonly said that the diesel engine would run on anything: crude oil, butter, cheese, or baloney—and in that talk a lot of the latter was used. The diesel engine wasn't a refuse consumer at all. It wasn't something made to use up the stuff you couldn't use in any other way. It was really a fundamental power-producing apparatus, and it was kept alive by the circumstance that it was more economical of fuel than other forms of motive power.

For years I was concerned about why the diesel engine didn't come along faster than it did. So in the 1920's I began to study it. For a time that study was a kind of intellectual golf game with me. I went around the circle, around and around, to find out what the real problem was. I made dozens of sketches. I then built a diesel-powered boat to study the engines in it, diesel engines which then weighed 125 pounds per horsepower.

Out of that analysis we set up the problem in this way: If the diesel engine is going to be of any great importance in the transportation industry, we must first set a top limit on weight. It shouldn't weigh any more than a gasoline engine of comparable power, or be any bigger. It should have the same degree of flexibility throughout the entire speed range as the corresponding gasoline engine.

Then someone said, "You are just wishing for something." But we all know that the only way you get anything is to wish for it and then work to get it. So we set up the "wish" and tried to see what we could do. We had accepted the higher pressure of the diesel engine, which meant that the parts had to be heavier. And, if you are to use the same number of heavy parts as light parts, the engine had to be heavier.

We therefore went to the two-cycle principle, in which the engine fires every time the piston comes up, instead of every other time, as the conventional four-cycle engine does. That meant that we only had to use half as many pieces for the same power. We have done that. It was a big job, and we had a lot of trouble. You can't start anything like that without getting into a lot of difficulties. But gradually the troubles were overcome.

So one of the fundamentals is that diesel engines do not have to be big and heavy. The weight was in somebody's head. We always want to blame our ignorance on the engine. Thus, after years of experimentation, we arrived at a light-weight, high-speed, two-cycle power plant that realized most of the diesel's theoretical efficiency.

One of the big problems in the diesel engine is how to inject the fuel into the cylinders in as finely divided a state as possible. We started out with the idea that if we could raise the fuel injection pressure from the usual four or five thousand pounds to twenty or twenty-five thousand, we could still further subdivide the fuel and thus get better control of the burning process.

I suppose that no one ever started anything new that someone didn't tell him that he couldn't do it. And that was true in this instance. A good many years ago I was running a test down in Kentucky, and we happened to arrive at a railroad crossing at a time when there had been an accident in which a railroad train had hit the rear of a buggy and injured one of the occupants. The occupants were a mother and her daughter, and the daughter had received a bad cut on her forehead. We volunteered to take the mother and daughter a few miles to a small town to a hospital there, where the cut could be treated.

There the doctor looked at the wound, saw that some stitches were needed, and said, "I think I will use a local anesthetic here."

"What is that?" said the mother.

"That is something so she won't feel the pain when I am sewing up this cut," replied the doctor.

"You cain't do that," said the mother. "I ain't never heard of it."

And you know we are very much that way today. If we ain't heard of it, it hain't, and we "ain't heard" much of anything yet.

Our difficulty was that, if we were going to try to pump fuel oil at a pressure of 25,000 pounds per square inch, we couldn't put packing around the plunger or piston as you do in regular oil or water pumps to keep it from leaking. The only way you could pack that piston so the oil wouldn't leak by it was to make the clearance between the cylinder and the piston smaller than the diameter of an oil molecule. We had to make our injector plungers fit that closely because, if we didn't, the fuel oil would leak by the plungers when the pressure was applied and the oil wouldn't get into the cylinders.

It is very simple. Out there, say, is a door of a certain size. Now we start to bring the sides of the door in and make it smaller and smaller, or narrower and narrower. Finally, we will trap some of the big fellows in this room. If we are going to keep all the people from getting out of here, we have to make a door that is narrower than the smallest person. And, if you are going to keep fuel oil from leaking by a piston you have to make the clearance smaller than the smallest oil molecule. And that isn't very big, you know.

In this you are talking about millionths of an inch. It used to be that a human hair, which has a diameter of about three-thousandths of an inch, was thought of as a very small dimension. Here is a good way to illustrate the dimensions we had to deal with. Pull a hair out of your head—if you happen to have a hair—and sit down with a nice sharp razor and slice that hair up into 120 shavings of equal thickness. And one of those shavings would be the clearance permissible between the piston and cylinder of our injector.

Well, we succeeded in making these injectors. And once in Grand Rapids, where these diesel fuel injectors are being manufactured, the wife of a doctor said to me, "Did you know that during the war I worked at the injector plant and had charge of inspecting some of the injector parts?"

"Did you realize how closely you were measuring?" I asked.

She said, "No, I didn't. There were just two bars and a mirror, and the hand of the gauge had to come between them."

"Well," I said, "you were measuring with an accuracy of only a few millionths of an inch."

This lady did not have an engineering or a practical education. It was the exactness of the tool that made it possible for her to do that inspection operation. And in this you can see how tooling for precision manufacturing is very, very important.

In 1933, two of those newly developed two-cycle diesel engines of ours were placed in operation at the Century of Progress Exposition in Chicago to run electrical generators for the General Motors exhibit. It was then that a very able railroad man, Ralph Budd of the Burlington, came to us because he knew that the railroad industry just had to have the sort of lightweight power which those new diesels supplied. He asked us to work out their application to railroad operation as power for small fast passenger trains he wanted to try. We went to work on that job, adapting the diesel engine to turn an electric generator and the electricity so produced ran motors which propelled the train. When our first diesel-electric locomotive went into operation propelling those little three-car trains, it marked the launching of the streamliners. Our contribution was the development of a type of diesel engine light enough in proportion to the horsepower it produced not to overload the locomotive.

At the outset the railroads did not accept this new type of motive power as an assured article of commerce at all, but they were ready to try an experiment. One railroad man made the statement that they bought the first small streamline train not as an investment but as an advertisement, because they had to do something spectacular to get the American people to look at the railways again.

But when they put out that train it was interesting to everybody. The public, newspapers, magazines, technical journals, and everything else could not keep from saying something about it. One railroad man said that, for the advertising we have received, we could afford to buy one of those little trains, run it for a short period of time, and push it into the Grand Canyon. However, they found out that those new-type trains were one of the best revenue getters of anything they had ever had. So they were kept in operation.

This was, in fact, the opening of a new era in the powering of railroad transportation. Only four years after the first small streamliner, a railroad man said to me: "You know, this thing didn't turn out the way we expected it to at all. When we went into this diesel railway business, we wanted to build some small three-car trains to take the place of buses, because we thought we could handle such traffic better on the railroad."

Now, just a few years later, he had ended up with a super-de-luxe train, a hotel on wheels, with comforts and conveniences not found in some hotels. The first diesel-powered trains had 600 horsepower of engine in them and three cars. This new train had 5,400 horsepower in the locomotive. Two supplementary diesel engines in the baggage car serviced the train. The locomotive could leave the train in the middle of the desert with the thermometer at 120 degrees, but, thanks to the air conditioning, the passengers would be perfectly comfortable as long as they stayed aboard.

I said to that railroad president, "What on earth did you build these fine big trains for if that is just opposite of what you set out to do?"

"This is what the people want," he replied. And there is the whole story. But the people couldn't tell him what they wanted until he had given them a sample. You don't know about anything until you make a sample of it and let the public decide what they want.

For years the passenger train schedule from Chicago to the West Coast had been 72 hours. When the diesel locomotive made a 39-hour schedule possible old-timers said that if you put these high-speed trains on the track you are going to delay all your freight trains to let the fast passenger trains pass or have the right of way. And the delays in freight would cost the railroads more than the faster passenger service could yield. But this did not happen. Even with the faster schedule, the diesel-powered locomotives could accelerate so rapidly and attain speed with such ease that they had enough cushion, so that when necessary they could even be given the siding to let a freight train pass in the opposite direction.

Then in early 1941 diesel-freight locomotives began to go into service and with them freight trains moved faster than they did before. Diesel-powered switchers had come simultaneously with the streamliners. And with the freight locomotive we had the entire range of the railroad motive power field covered. Thus, the nation entered World War II with the advantages of diesel power available for the faster movement of men and *matériel*.

You always have conservative people. And among the things they said as to why the diesel-powered locomotive would not be practicable was that you never could take the locomotive engineer away from a steam engine and get him to drive this new-fangled thing. Even some psychologists said they would bet 10 to 1 on that. Well, they were just 10 to 1 wrong. Once the engineer who had been operating a steam locomotive for a long while got into the cab of one of these diesel locomotives—where he had a comfortable seat, a windshield of safety glass with wiper, defroster, sunglare shield, and no-draft windows, and where he could work with clean clothes and a white collar—he said, "Who would want to run one of those steam locomotives again?" There was even difficulty getting some of the older engineers to give them up and take their retirement when the time for it came.

In 1938 at the dedication in Chicago of the "Capitol Limited," a diesel-drawn train between Chicago and Washington, one of the railroad officials there mentioned an interesting thing. His grandfather drove the horses that pulled the first railway car in America, he said. It was on a line 15 miles long out of Baltimore. Then his father drove the first steam engine on the Baltimore and Ohio. Now the third generation was one of the pioneers in the diesel trains.

With the small diesel-powered trains which the railroads put on at first there were predictions that you would have to keep the right of way absolutely clear of snow, because if the train should hit a snowdrift it would be thrown off the track. There were two of those light trains running between Chicago and Minneapolis and St. Paul, which made a round trip every day, a distance of 880 miles. That winter of 1935 the weather got colder and colder until they were not able to get the snowplows out. One of the diesel trains was behind time one day and the engineer, supposing that the track was clear of snow and trying to get on schedule, speeded around a curve into a cut that was full of snow. He just shut his eyes and thought of his wife and family and felt that this was going to be the end of it all. But nothing happened! He never felt the train hit the snowdrift. When he opened his eyes he was still on the track going very, very fast.

Then they found out that by hitting a snowdrift at 85 miles an hour it didn't cause any trouble. So they used the high-speed trains to clear the tracks for the steam locomotive. And so spectacular it was that some very nice motion pictures of it were taken. Of course, you couldn't have gotten anybody to go out and try that for the first time. It had to be an accident, and most of the good things we do are accidents.

There is a saying that you can't teach an old dog new tricks. That depends on how old the dog is. Colonel George H. Emerson, chief of motive power and equipment for one of the nation's major railroads, was eighty-three years old at the time of the following event. He had been one of the great steam engine designers of this country. When we got our first demonstration model of a diesel locomotive for freight service, he said: "I know the limitations of railroad equipment and I think you have something new. I want to borrow that freight locomotive. I want to test it out down in Virginia and I want you fellows to go along."

We went down there, and on the track he had 250 carloads of coal all coupled together and with the slack pulled out. A hundred and fifty people from his railroad were there too.

"Hitch your diesel locomotive on to that string of cars," he directed the operator of it.

"You know you can't start 250 carloads of coal that way," he was told.

"I know you can't, but I want you to couple on to it anyway."

"You know what will happen," I said. "It will pull a drawbar out. You know that."

"Nobody in the railroad business has ever seen a drawbar *pulled* out," he replied. "They have seen a few *jerked* out, but none pulled out. We are going to pull one out."

We did just that. Then, at his insistence, we pulled out another drawbar, and still another.

When that same thing had been done three times, Colonel Emerson said: "That is enough. It will cost me three thousand dollars to have those drawbars put back. But, to show you how profitable this demonstration has been, it will save six hundred thousand dollars' worth of arguments. So it is very cheap. Everybody has been saying that the diesel locomotive has no power. Now the argument will be that it has too much power, but everybody knows how to fix that."

We used to sit around the table and say, "How long should these diesel locomotives run before they need to be overhauled? How long should the piston rings last? How long should the pistons last?" Remember that most of the fellows in on this diesel development were automobile men. They finally reached the idea that if pistons had to be changed at 50,000 miles that would be pretty good. And if they had to put the engine in the roundhouse only each 100,000 miles that would be pretty good too.

After the first nonstop run from Chicago to Denver, we were sitting in the Brown Palace Hotel there in the morning and Mr. Ralph Budd of the Union Pacific Railroad said to me, "How often do you think these engines should go to the roundhouse? Do you think 100,000 miles would be all right?

"If I were your engineer," I said, "I would think that would be perfectly terrible." Remember that some of them ran a thousand miles every day.

"Well, we don't have anything now that will do that well," he said.

But today, with the progress made meanwhile, piston rings are running 500,000 miles in railroad service before they need to be changed. And the engines need to go to the back shop, as it is called in railroad lingo, to be fitted with new pistons and liners only once in a million and a half miles.

Someone once asked me, "What is the drawbar pull of a diesel locomotive?"

"I don't know just what it is in pounds," I said. "But railroad men tell me that it has been strong enough to pull a good many railroads out of the hands of receivers."

So effective have diesel locomotives been in reducing operating costs and improving services that they have literally paid for themselves out of direct savings over steam operation. In fuel efficiency alone diesel locomotives haul goods with five times the efficiency of steam locomotives. How fortunate it was for the railroads that the diesel engine was freed of its weight shackles as early as it was.

Although the railroads are again not as healthy as they would like to be, it is not because of their motive power. The diesel smashed the old roadblock of steam and revolutionized rail transportation, giving it new life for a long period.[1] In less than fifteen years after its introduction, the high-speed diesel made obsolete an engine which had been used and perfected for more than a century.

---

[1] Said in 1958.

I AM AN OLD PILOT

Kettering was one of the pioneers of aviation, especially in his major role as an early and enthusiastic booster of the airplane. After having flown for seven years, he began in 1919 to fly airplanes himself, and at one time he had more hours in the air than any other amateur pilot. Everything in this chapter he said either within that pioneering phase of aviation—during the first twenty years of the airplane—or later on in speaking about those first two decades.

Many years later, however, still "sold on" flying, Kettering made this prediction about the future of the airplane: "Nothing can stop it from becoming the greatest form of transportation."

I AM AN OLD PILOT. I TOOK MY FIRST AIRPLANE FLIGHT IN 1912 and I have made a great many thousand flights since that time. The last flight I have taken is the most wonderful thing I have ever done, and it has been that way ever since I first started to fly.

About the time I was going to college there were two home-trained mechanics running a little bicycle shop in Dayton, Ohio, Wilbur and Orville Wright. They had the fantastic idea that man could build a machine in which he could fly. They watched the birds and tinkered with homemade motors. A sister who taught school helped them with her savings, and they just kept at it. People laughed at them, but they went right on. They wouldn't be licked. And sure enough, they did fly.

It is difficult now to picture the state of mind of the people before the coming of the airplane. A common expression of the day was, "You might as well try to *fly* as do that."

For hundreds of years, man had dreamed of mechanical flight and even written poems about it. I wonder how many people remember "Darius Green and His Flying Machine"? To fly was the ambition of the ages.

But as the result of hundreds of failures, formulas had been developed and books written to prove that man could not fly. A smoke screen had been thrown around the entire subject to hide these failures. Yet, if anyone had taken the trouble to look out of the window, he would have seen birds flying over the landscape. But, of course, birds didn't know all of those reasons why it couldn't be done; so they just flew anyway.

But this smoke screen of failure didn't fool everyone. Those two men in Dayton were sure the facts were being hidden. So they experimented with kites and gliders and finally put a gasoline engine of their own make in an airplane. They used calculations to find out how it could be done, not why it was impossible. And they flew right through that smoke screen of impossibility.

Any new thing always comes in with a prejudice. I happen to have known the history of the aircraft business from the time it started because I knew the Wright brothers when they were my neighbors in Dayton. Those boys were interested in gliders. So they got a book on gliders written by a German by the name of Otto Lilienthal. Lilienthal was killed trying out his theories, but in his book he had written so interestingly about gliding that they thought that for their next year's vacation they would build a glider. They didn't do this as an avocation, they did it as a vacation.

Since for gliding you need a little breeze, they wrote to the Post Office Department, because we had no weather department then, asking about some place where there is a lot of sand. They wanted something soft to land on in case the glider didn't work, and they needed wind of about 30 miles an hour. After several weeks the Post Office Department wrote that the wind averaged 30 miles an hour at Kitty Hawk, North Carolina.

And so that is the reason they went to Kitty Hawk. Orville Wright told me that the figures for the wind there were about right. They did have an average wind of 30 miles an hour. The wind blew 60 miles an hour one day and did not blow at all the next day, which shows that you want to be careful about averages.

The boys went down to North Carolina to try out their glider.

They did not succeed so well that first year, although they did get a few little glides. They found that the wings weren't exactly right and that there were few reliable figures that could be used in calculating their wing and control surfaces.

So they built the first wind tunnel. It was made of parts of a store box and an electric fan. Then they developed instruments for measuring the effects of wind on these surfaces and planes. They spent many months testing various wing shapes in their little wind tunnel. In 1901 they tested over 200 different types and developed the first practical data on the curved shape of air foils, as they are called. It is interesting to note that today, with our very large wind tunnels, our use of thousands of horsepower and the finest types of instruments, the Wright brothers' results of that time are still found to be approximately correct.

They finally made a pretty good wing, and then they said, "If we had a motor on this thing with a propeller, we could fly." In those days, in 1903, we did not know as much about engines as we do now. And so they wrote to some well-known automobile companies asking them to build a light engine of about ten or twelve horsepower with which to fly this airplane. None of those concerns had time to do it because they were very busy; and, of course, anybody who wanted an engine for an airplane was foolish anyhow. So why build it for them?

Thus the Wright boys had to build their own engine. Well, all the machinery they had in their bicycle shop was a drill press and a lathe. Everybody knows that you cannot make an engine on a drill press and a lathe. But they did not know that. So they went ahead and built an engine that worked very well.

With that engine, which gave them twelve horsepower, they equipped their first airplane and they went to Kitty Hawk. The first successful flight with a heavier-than-air machine was made there on the seventeenth of December, 1903. Afterwards, they sent a telegram to their sister Catharine in Dayton, saying that they had had a wonderful day, that they had flown successfully in an engine-powered airplane, and that they would be home for Christmas.

When Catharine Wright got that momentous telegram she was quite excited about it. She took down the telephone and called a Dayton newspaper. This was about eleven o'clock at night and the telephone rang and rang and rang. The boys were playing pinochle, I suppose, or something like that, and they had to wait until the hand was out before they could answer. At last, one of the fellows took down the receiver and said, "Well?"

She said, "This is Catharine Wright speaking. I have just had a telegram from my brothers." So she read it to him, and the fellow said, "Good. I'm glad to know the boys are going to get home for Christmas," and he hung up the receiver.

The man who answered the telephone that night was the one who told me the story. He said, "I was a perfectly normal human being at the time. Everybody knew you couldn't fly, because time and time again it had been proved mathematically that you couldn't fly anything heavier than air. In the next place, everybody knew the Wright brothers were crazy."

But it hadn't been proved *experimentally* that you couldn't fly. The Wright brothers were willing to try.

If you had gone back and sat with Wilbur and Orville Wright at the time they were getting ready to try to fly, you would have thought that flying had no future whatever. At Kitty Hawk the Wright boys roomed at the Coast Guard station. More than thirty-five years afterwards the man who was captain of the station at that time told me that another government man said to him then, "If I were you, I wouldn't let those fellows stay around my house. In a little while you are going to be classed with them yourself, and everybody knows they are crazy."

Nearly five years after the famous first flight at Kitty Hawk, Wilbur Wright went to France to give a demonstration of the airplane to the group that had taken an option on their European patents. Through the help of the French automobile manufacturer, Léon Bollée, Wilbur obtained the use of the Le Mans racecourse as a flying field. And, on August 8, 1908, a large crowd had gathered to witness the flight.

In this crowd were many skeptics. One in particular was Ernest Archdeacon of the Aero Club of France.[1] While Wright was adjusting his machine, Archdeacon was explaining to the people seated in the grandstand what was wrong with the airplane and why it could never work. He said that Wright knew this and was just bluffing.

But the Frenchman was suddenly interrupted by the loud applause and cheering of those in front of him as they shouted, "This man has conquered the air! He's no bluffer!" As Archdeacon turned, he was just in time to see Wright's plane clearing the tops of some trees in the distance.

We have not really awakened yet to a realization of what aviation is.[2] If we talked about everything the way we do about aviation, we would still be riding around in oxcarts. I have said time and again that we have a lot of people riding around in automobiles who have oxcart minds.

Everyone ought to take a ride in an airplane. If an airplane passenger has any personal conceit, such an experience will remove it before he again reaches the ground. If one is general manager of some great factory, reaches an altitude of 5,000 feet, looks back and sees a little bit of a factory about the size of a postage stamp, he is bound to realize that he is not so much, after all. Nothing else in the world will give one such a perspective of the relationship of individual activities to world activities as a flight in an airplane. I said, the first time I went up, that it looked very foolish to quarrel about 2 feet on a line fence, one side or the other.

The pleasure of travel by air is almost indescribable. At 125 miles an hour your impression of speed is about 3 miles an hour in the going. You actually have no sensation of speed or height at all. You get a beautiful panorama of the country. With a few maps

---

[1] An organization devoted then to lighter-than-air craft.
[2] Said in 1921 at the Annual Dinner of the Society of Automotive Engineers, Hotel Astor, New York.

in front of you, you can look at your watch and say to yourself, "In half an hour I ought to be in such and such a place." And in that time the town comes along. With maps you can put your pencil down on right where you are.

A great many people think it must be a hard thing to keep a machine in the air. With the modern high-speed cross-country machine, a pilot doesn't do anything after he gets in the air. He can get up and leave his seat and indulge in a smoke if he wants to. Travelers can lounge around, talk to their companions, read, and do anything they could do on a railroad train. They can travel as comfortably and as safely as in a high-grade motorcar. A lot of people don't believe it. Progress is always a degree of insanity, more or less.

We do not think of the airplane as important today because but few know of its wonderful possibilities. I made only two railroad trips last year. I flew more than 15,000 miles. I was not out joy-riding. I was just at one place and wanted to go somewhere else, and I traveled in an airplane.

Permit me to tell you an incident. I had to be in Philadelphia on Monday. I left there Monday night on a fast Pennsylvania express that goes to St. Louis. I got off the train at Dayton, Ohio, shortly before eight o'clock Tuesday morning,[3] went home, had breakfast, repacked my bag, went down to the field, got into an airplane, and we were out here in Witchita, Kansas, two hours before that train was in St. Louis. I do not care what you think about flying or about the airplane. There is an economic fact which all the skepticism of the world cannot push aside.

A lot of people say, "You will never get me up in an airplane." I had a fine example of that week before last when I entertained the Operating and Finance Committees of General Motors. They were on hand to go over our program of research for the next year, and I said: "We will finish the meeting at four o'clock and for all

[3] July 17, 1919.

those who want to take an airplane ride, we will have three machines over here and they can do it."

The president of the company was there, and he said, "Now look here, Kettering, there is to be none of this flying with this gang. We can't stop *you;* you are too far gone. But none of this bunch is going to fly."

I said, "What do you want to bet?"

One fellow said, "There isn't money enough in the world to get me off the ground." But we went out to the airplanes. And, when you opened them up and stepped in, it was different. You stepped inside just as you did into your limousines, and you didn't have to put on any flying togs or anything like that. And the men said, "Gee, this looks pretty nice!"

"Well," I said, "better just take a little ride." Before we got through, the whole gang, the president and everybody else, was flying. But the funniest joke was that everybody wanted to fly home.

This was a group of men who couldn't afford to fly—they were too important. But when they got one taste of it you know there was nothing to keep them from it at all. When they took a flight they began to realize that it wasn't any hazard. And I honestly don't think you take any chance in a decent airplane, with a pilot that hasn't got stunt ideas. There is just as much sense to stunting in an airplane as there is to running down the street in an automobile, putting on the brakes, and skidding around the corner. I have always had a rule for myself: Never fly when the birds don't, because they have had a lot of experience.

Several years hence the aircraft industry will be a big business.[4] It is in its infancy, but it is developing. It is a real institution. A means of transportation which is from three to five times faster than any other is a utility. It is such a great utility that we do not at first appreciate it.

Regardless of what your opinion may be about keeping your feet on the ground, you are going to get up in the air. You are going to

---

[4] Said in 1920 in a speech at Philadelphia.

fly, not because you want to but because in the future the economy of business will make it as necessary for you to fly as it was necessary for you to drop the horse and buggy and take to an automobile. This is only one of the phases of the great scientific development that is coming in this country. We must accept it with an open mind.

You have heard the theory that necessity is the mother of invention. The Wright brothers didn't build their airplane because there was a necessity to. They built it because they wanted to learn how to fly. Up to that time nobody had been able to.

I believe the Wright brothers wanted to fly for one reason. They wanted to prove that man could do whatever the birds could, and they wanted to be the *first* ones to do it. The only reward they could expect would be satisfaction—*satisfaction of accomplishment*. It is this intense desire to succeed that gives men, such as the Wrights, the courage and the patience to overcome every obstacle, every failure, every disappointment that always go hand in hand with the development of any new thing.

Regardless of whether the pioneer is a mathematician in ancient Greece, a composer, a painter, or a research worker in a modern industry, this outlook—if he is to succeed—must be fundamentally the same. He will have to possess patience, courage, and open-mindedness. Desire to solve the problem must be strong enough to overcome any existing difficulties and he should not be discouraged by the endless hours needed to get the facts. And, whatever the compensation, the enduring satisfaction of solving the problem is worth many times the financial reward or world acclaim. And, regardless of its method or origin, the work remains as a lasting heritage to the generations that follow.

So the Wright brothers didn't see in their first experimental flying machines the possibilities of commercial airlines, bombers, or private planes for John Smith.

No, I think they just wanted to fly!

WHY IS THE GRASS GREEN?

All his life, from the time he was a boy on the farm, Kettering was intensely interested in plants and how they grow. That interest led him to set up at Antioch College in 1930 an effort to find an answer to the question, "Why is the grass green?" His purpose was to learn just how nature builds the energy of sunshine into plants and how that wealth of sunshine might be utilized to a larger extent in producing food and fuel.

He pursued that investigation for nearly thirty years, during the last decade of his life directly in a laboratory of his own. Within that time, knowledge of how nature performs her great miracle was advanced a great deal. The full answer to the question, though, has not been found even yet. But along the way Kettering often talked about the endeavor, and to the end of his life in 1958 he continued to be just as optimistic as ever about the ultimate success of the search.

I WAS BORN AND RAISED ON A FARM. I AM GLAD OF IT AND I WISH sometimes I had stayed there.

I was sent to school by my parents because farm work was hard. "We want you to get an education," they said, "so that you won't have to work as hard as we do." Well, I had a chance to tell my father and mother before they died that they certainly missed their wish. I am working day and night and Sundays, and they had Sunday afternoon off.

I am enthusiastic about being an American because I came from the hills in Ohio. I was a hillbilly. We each had one pair of boots a year, and we didn't put them on too soon in the fall because we had to decide which we would sooner do, run around in the frosty grass a little more in the fall or in the wet snow in the spring.

Now, I didn't know at that time that I was an underpriviliged person because I had to drive the cows through the frosty grass—

and stand in a nice warm spot where a cow had lain to warm my feet. I thought that was wonderful. I walked three miles back and forth each day to the high school in a little village and I thought that was wonderful, too. I thought of all that as opportunity, and I thought the only thing involved in opportunity was whether I knew how to think with my head and how to do with my hands. I thought that was what opportunity consisted of. I didn't know you had to have money. I didn't know you had to have all these luxuries that we want everybody to have today.

I am enthusiastic about being an American, too, because I have seen the progress that has been made on the farm. I have seen all these things develop: the tractors, the reapers, the binders, the electric light, the telephone, the radio. Today the farmers in the neighborhood of my youth are very up-to-date and, because of fine highways, they are an integral part of the community. That community has not had to go out and get these things—they have come to it. The radio and other developments appeared there almost as soon as in New York and Chicago.

On the farm I liked particularly the job of working corn. In fact, I liked everything about raising corn, planting it, plowing it, cutting it, and everything else. I was the best darn corn cutter in Ohio. I liked to go barefoot when plowing corn. The ground felt so good, even though once in a while a fellow did hit a stone.[1]

My father and I were plowing corn one day alongside the road when a neighbor came by in his wagon and stopped to chat a while, as farmers do. To my father he said, "Jake, I sold my hogs today."

"Did you?" my father replied. "How did they weigh?"

"Well, you know, they didn't weigh as much as I thought they would—and I didn't have any idea that they would either."

Our nation is one of the few countries in the world that has a surplus of food. I think, too, that ours is one of the few countries

---

[1] The time spoken of here was about 1895, well before that when modern machinery came to the farm.

where people are worrying for fear they eat too much. One of our problems is to know what is the proper diet so you can lose weight, not gain it. We have so much food that it has become a political issue. This is one of the calamitous situations we have gotten ourselves into. How did we come to do that?

Well, for one thing, in the past several years we have taken twenty million horses off American farms. Every time you don't feed a horse, you can feed four and a half people. Of course, it's a little hard on the horses; but, because of it, we can feed ninety million more people without farming any more land.

Now what took the horses off the farm? Right away, a fellow will say, "The farm tractor." But we have had tractors for fifty years. It was two inventions that let the tractor take the horses off the farm. These were the pneumatic tire and those two little angularly set wheels at the front of the tractor which let you come up to the end of a row crop, such as a corn crop, turn as sharp as a horse can, and go back down the next row. This is what took the horses off the farm.

That tricycle steering gear is a simple thing. It never gets mentioned in anybody's book as a great invention, and yet it is one of the things largely responsible for our tremendous excess of food, the overweight people, and the political issues.

Much has been said about the depletion of our soil. This is a scientific problem of long standing. I believe that, if necessity demands, we can go to our inexhaustible supply of minerals in the sea for all the plant food we will ever need to keep our farm land productive, just as we have gone to the air for nitrogen. Only about 2½ per cent, by weight, of a plant is mineral. We have learned how to obtain salts and bromine from the sea commercially. The extraction of millions of pounds of bromine annually from the sea is an important chemical development of recent years. But there is only 1 pound of bromine to about 8 tons of sea water.

Here is a real challenge to future generations to become chemists and engineers of the sea. I remember that when I was a boy on the farm the farmers were worrying about what they would do for rail fences when the woods were all cut down. But, long before the woods were gone, we had wire fences and nobody built a rail fence.

The sun does three things. It grows our vegetables, it pumps the water to run our rivers, and it makes the high-tension lightning that knocks out our public services. Practically everything that ever moved on the earth has been moved by energy which came directly from the sun.[2]

We do not know, except in a very superficial way, how the energy which is given out by the sun is transmitted to the earth. We do not know how plants pick up this energy and convert the inanimate carbon dioxide and water into vital materials so necessary for our existence. This, when understood, will open up an entirely new conception of things that can be done.[3]

To illustrate the tremendous energy we receive from the sun, a black plate held in the sun at midday will be heated to some 175 degrees F. When the sun goes down, though, the plate cools off. Now what we need is a process by which this energy that heats the plate can be saved. That is exactly what a plant does. It is the only way we have of keeping some of the sun's energy down here so we can use it next winter when it gets cold. In looking forward, one of our great problems is to see what we can do to improve the process by trapping a greater percentage of this solar energy.

The great receiving set is the leaf of a plant, and if it wasn't for that plant we wouldn't be here. Yet today, in this age in which we call ourselves scientific, we know just exactly nothing about

---

[2] Said in 1918.
[3] Said at a symposium on "Science and Industry in the Coming Century" held in 1934. On the same occasion he said this also: "It is not difficult with this information in hand for even the most unimaginative person to predict the propulsion of airplanes by radiant energy with the power plants located on the ground."

how the leaf of a plant is able to pick up the radiant energy from the sun and convert it into new chemical compounds.

But the leaves of plants fix billions of tons of carbon every year. Nature has devised a means of taking two low-energy compounds, water and carbon dioxide, with energy from the sun, to build our entire plant life in all its variations. And remember that there are only three one-hundredths of 1 per cent of carbon dioxide in the air.

Nature does all this without a test tube, without a burette, without a chemical balance, without a log table or a slide rule or anything else. In fact, nature never had a college education. We can't do any of those reactions yet, but nature has been doing them since long before man was in existence.

When you mention the word "chemistry" you always think of some place that has a lot of bottles and bad smells. I think we have got to get out of that state of mind, because everything you touch is chemistry. Material is chemistry, that is all it is. Water running under a bridge is a chemical, just the same as it is in a bottle with H_2O on the label. So we must get chemistry out of the laboratory and we must live chemistry in the terms that it is everything.

It has long seemed to me that one of the big problems we have is to find out how the sun does this trick of building up plant life —how does the plant fix the sun's energy into chemical compounds? One may say that this is one of the things the Lord never intended us to find out about. Well, He is certainly not trying to keep it a secret because He has it around everywhere.

When, many years ago, I began research on the growth of plants, we performed a very elementary experiment. We got sea sand and heated it in an old-fashioned iron kettle up to about 350 degrees to kill all the organisms in it. Then we washed it with water, with acid, with alkali, and then with water again, until it consisted only of inert material.

We put that sand in red flowerpots which we had boiled and cleaned up also, and planted seeds in them. Then from a burette we dripped into that potted sand a standardized solution of plant food. What the plant didn't use ran through into a beaker and was analyzed to find what the plant had taken out.

This showed that different plants wanted different ingredients. An interesting thing was that when the plant bloomed it changed its formula, and when it began to grow fruit it changed its formula again. So we tried the experiment of not supplying to it in the feeding solution the material required for the bloom formula. In that way we could grow stalks just as big as we wanted without bloom, or we could change the formula to bring flowers on little plants. We raised some cucumbers so large that I didn't dare tell about them because everybody thought I was lying.

For many years I have been studying the subject of photosynthesis and chlorophyll. Those are big words which sound as though we must be a smart bunch of fellows. When we say photosynthesis, we say the effect of light, and chlorophyll is the Greek word for green leaf. But we don't know any more about the green leaf in Greek than we do in English—not a bit. So, when this investigation was begun at Antioch College many years ago, I told the boys, "Let's make it simple. We will just ask the question: Why is the grass green?"

I told the men, too: "I want you all to get married and have a lot of children, because I think this is about a three-generation job. I shall not be disappointed if I have to die without knowing, because I think some generation soon will know."

Why is the grass green? That is a very important question. But a lot of people look at you in astonishment. They say, "Everybody knows why the grass is green."

"Well," I said, "I don't. Why isn't it blue?"

After having worked for years to find out why the grass is green, the only really good answer I have got came from a fellow who ran a golf club in Arizona. He said, "I don't know what you have in mind, but out here the only thing that makes grass green is water. If I don't water those greens, they turn brown."

But we don't know how a blade of grass grows. We don't know anything about a stalk of corn. And that growth is quite a miracle. You plant a grain of corn and in ninety days it will weigh many, many times as much as the grain you planted. If you burn the stalk of corn, the ash will weigh only about 2½ per cent of the total weight of the stalk. And, if you put that ash back in the ground, you can raise another stalk of corn the next year.

In other words, about 98 per cent of that stalk of corn was simply combined from the air and the water and the sunshine. It was the sunshine that did the work. So agriculture is not farming merely so many acres of ground. It is so many acres plus sunlight.

For many years I wondered about the people who live in the tropics. If you had given an engineer, with his modern ideas, the job of designing people to live there, they would be white and the chances are they would have a coating of aluminum paint to reflect the sunlight. And yet, all the people who live in the tropics are dark. So we must be wrong because nature doesn't make very many mistakes.

Now we think we know why that is, and it is quite elementary. If you eat a lot of uncooked fruits or vegetables, you can become sensitized to light. Consequently, the people who live in the tropics are the ones who are not sensitive to light.

We have taken some ordinary guinea pigs, white and black, and sensitized them. They sensitize very easily. All you need to do is to feed them a few grains of raw buckwheat each day for a week. Then when they go out in the sunlight the black one is perfectly all right; but the white guinea pig, if he stays out too long, will drop over dead. If, however, before the white guinea pig goes out, you put a black sweater on him, he is not harmed by the sunlight. Something in the buckwheat makes the guinea pigs sensitive to the sun.

In the presence of sunshine the leaf of the plant takes water and carbon dioxide, breaks them down, and builds up those marvelous carbohydrates and proteins about which we talk so glibly and know so little. Right here is the basis of all biology. So we started out to see if we could find anything at all about the mechanism of what goes on in the leaf of a plant.

Originally, we thought that the plant's great trick was its possession of the green compound, chlorophyll. That is why we thought we'd make our problem simple by naming the project, "Why is the grass green?" Chemists put on a big drive to discover the chemical structure of chlorophyll. They solved it, but didn't give us the answer to the question of how plants trap the sun's energy.

Now plants grew millions of years before we were here. And, of course, the plant has priority over us—or seniority, I should say—and it is difficult to find the elementary principle now. So some years ago in our research we began to feel that we couldn't get at the secret of photosynthesis by working on the leaf of the plant, because in that you are dealing with something so many millions of years old. And that therefore we would have to go clear back to the beginning and try to find out what existed before there was any biology.

We elected to approach it by presupposing that this earth of ours had been a hot place at one time and as it cooled down there was in time a condition of temperate radiance, but as yet no organic compounds. Our work then began to be done on the step prior to life—what was the mechanical or inorganic setup which, plus radiant energy, started growth? I called it prebiological organic chemistry, simply to get back ahead of the cell.

In some of our studies, too, we have been using the oldest plant on earth as our test specimen. It is called blue-green algae and is the green scum that grows on ponds in the summertime. This blue-green slime goes far, far back into prehistoric days, and hasn't changed its appearance in a million years. Also, it has a generation every two weeks; so you can get a lot of effect pretty fast.

A friend of mine who knew I was interested in algae was traveling abroad. There he came across a little book on the subject. He called me up on the overseas telephone, very excited, and said,

"Ket, I just picked up a little book fresh off the press over here and these fellows have really got it." Then he sent me the book by air mail. I opened it up and on the first line it said that the active principle of blue-green algae is phycocyanin.

I grabbed the telephone and asked one of my associates in our investigation to send me the structural formula of phycocyanin. I didn't get a reply right away. So I called him again and he said that nobody here knows the formula for phycocyanin. When I returned to my home in Dayton I looked up the word phycocyanin in my unabridged dictionary. Sure enough, there it was.

Phycocyanin, I read, came from the Greek *phykos* meaning seaweed and *cyanin* for blue. So I had gone out, walked around the house, and come back in through the same door. And I find that we know so many things just that way.

I have spent about thirty years on this question of why the grass is green. Somebody said to me the other day, "Don't you get discouraged? You've been many years on this investigation of photosynthesis and you haven't got anything, have you?"

My answer was that we have come up until we are only a little bit below zero on this thing now. We are just getting a perspective of what the problem really is. So in that field we are going to make tremendous advances. Much of what was known we have found to be wrong. We think we are beginning to shake out a few of the fallacies.

Why should we get worried about thirty years? We have geological data that show plants to be millions of years old. So what's thirty years?

It's something like the fellow who was digging in one of those dinosaur skeleton excavations. Someone asked him: "Have you any idea how old that skeleton is?"

"Yes, sir, it's thirty million and two years old," he said.

"Why, what do you mean thirty million and two years old?"

"Well, when we began digging here they told me it was thirty million years old, and we've been working two years."

So we have to recognize that we are just learning how to learn now. We don't know much. Therefore if we get back to the idea that we *can* know about these things, then we will open up a whole new world. The way plants grow can't be too complicated because it works every place.

Today, on the average, nature is fixing in vegetation only about one-tenth of 1 per cent of the sunlight it receives. If we can develop new ways of doing things so we could fix two-tenths of 1 per cent of the sun's energy, we would double the food supply of the world. That surely seems to be worth while. If we don't succeed in catching at least that much, it is because we are a little stupid up in the attic. And I don't think we are that bad. Only about 25 per cent of the people of the earth have ever had enough to eat. This opens a great field for technology and engineering. I have often said that a thing is scientific as long as you don't understand it. As soon as you do understand it, it isn't scientific any more.

There is no reason why we cannot convert sunshine without growing plants. We looked at birds until we learned how to fly, but there aren't any feathers on airplanes. In fact, with all the skill of all the aeronautical engineers in the world, we couldn't make one feather today—we don't need them either. And all of our science cannot make a leaf. If we can learn how to convert sunshine without growing plants we may be able to make the vital step toward abundance and peace. There will then be nothing to fight about.

Just as long as the sun shines we don't need to worry about our food or fuel, if we'll get busy and learn how to convert that sunshine to chemical energy. But we're going to have to learn more about how to catch this energy from the sun. If we starve to death or run out of fuel, it's our own fault.

The Kettering Foundation now has a fairly large group working on solar energy at our laboratory in Yellow Springs, Ohio.[4]

[4] Said in 1958.

The progress that has been made there encourages me greatly. I am confident that from the results we have already obtained we are on the right track and one of these days we will climb out of our mental rut and find out what makes the grass green.

WE HAMMER OUR CHESTS TOO MUCH

"One of the things that concerns me," Kettering would say, "is that we pound our chests and say, 'Look what we have done.' We haven't done very much yet, and we have a lot of things to do."

WE SOMETIMES DO A LITTLE CHEST HAMMERING AND BOAST of the great things we have accomplished in science, engineering, and other fields. We do that without recognizing that the earth and the stars were here, running, long before we got here and that we have contributed very little to it, outside of fighting among ourselves.

We did not do anything to make the trees, we did not do anything to make bugs and bees and butterflies. But, my God, when we do something, how we pound our chests! We invent a camera and get all excited about it. Yet we are looking at the camera with a couple of "cameras" that are a lot better than any that man ever made. We could not make a human eye in a million years, but what a wonderful thing a camera is, we think.

We have five senses. We can see, and our eyes look something like the camera we have invented. The ear, too, looks like something we have made and we think we know something about the machinery of the ear. But when it comes to the mechanism of smell and taste and touch we have not made anything like any of these. So there are at least two of our senses, and probably three, about which we do not know anything at all, and we only think we know about the other two. After all, all we are doing is discovering what nature did a long time ago. We don't know the first principle about why the plant grows; and yet, if it didn't grow, we wouldn't be here. Thus there is something wrong with the man who is egotistical in the face of nature.

I was listening to some astronomers the other day, and I said,

201

"When did you fellows complete the job of putting the stars up there?"

"What do you mean?" they asked. And I said, "The way you fellows talk you would think that you had set the stars up there. I thought they had been there a long time."

Consider this modern wonder, radio. We look upon that as a brand new thing. Yet a man will go out and look at the moon and not think anything about it, although he is getting a message many times more wonderful and he is getting it by the finest radio receiver. Radio is nothing compared with sight.[1] You not only get a message with your eyes as receivers. You can point your finger to the exact spot from which the message is coming and you measure the wavelength in which it comes, because that is all color is.

We think we are conquering nature. Yet I have noticed that, whenever anyone speaks of conquering nature, what he really means is that he has got right down on his knees and done exactly what nature wanted done under the circumstances. Those fundamental laws of nature have been in operation ever since the world started, and we only discover them. When we do discover them, we think we did it. If you can get nature to do anything she doesn't want to do, I would like to know about it.

The noted stage comedian, Joe Cook, used to have an act in which he demonstrated an invention of his. It was a shower bath in which you could take a shower without undressing or getting wet, he said. He had it set up on the stage with the blueprints and all, and in the act he finally got a fellow from off the street to come in and try out the invention. Joe turned on the water and the fellow came out completely soaked. Whereupon Joe examined the apparatus very carefully and then said: "The only thing I can think of is that I must have overestimated my ability."

You have nothing to do with a chemical reaction, for example. You can pour two things together, but they are going to do exactly what the rules and regulations of those two particular things say

---

[1] Said in 1921.

they are going to do. You can help them by warming them up or cooling them off a little, and that is about all.

Man is very vain now about vitamins; he has made a great discovery. If vitamins hadn't been there all the time, he would never have been able to discover them. But he is never going to give the vitamins credit for letting him discover them.

I have spent some time working with the spectroscope. It is a marvelous means of identifying things in extremely small concentrations. But I also come from the hills of Ohio where we used to hunt a little, and I think of a hunting dog, an old hound, who far excelled the spectroscope in ability to detect minute quantities. He would sniff down a road where ten people had walked, turn down the right lane, and go into the house where his master was. He did that just by smell. Of course, he was a dumb animal. He had no college degree or anything else.

That is one of our difficulties right there, the dumb animal idea. The birds and bees and butterflies have been flying for hundreds of thousands of years. They must have a continual tickle when they see us trying to fly.

You heard recently about our flying a plane to England and back with a wonderful "automatic pilot." Well, every bee has an automatic pilot. The word "beeline" has been handed down to us as an accurate description of the most direct path through space. And this expression is based on repeated observations of the flight of bees.

Recent investigations have definitely proved that the bee has a directional control system as accurate and sensitive as the automatic pilots on our huge airplanes. There is, however, one outstanding difference. We have just developed our control apparatus within recent years. The bee has been using automatically controlled flight for millions of years.

Thus it appears that we are some millions of years behind nature in the control of flight—something we think of as being exclusively man-made. But as yet we are just infants in aerial navigation. We have been working on it for less than fifty years. For thousands of years birds have been making long overwater flights, as for example from Alaska to the Hawaiian Islands. Every year they arrive at precisely the same spot with perfect timing.

Many times I have taken carrier pigeons or homing pigeons from Dayton and Springfield, Ohio, when I was driving to Detroit. Just before getting to Detroit I would let them loose. They had made the trip up in a darkened cage and there was no way they could see the route by which they had come. But the pigeons brought from Dayton flew back to Dayton and those that came from Springfield flew the 200 miles to Springfield.

The bat is a very old creature. He, too, has this navigation business down fine. If you take two wheels revolving in opposite directions, and blindfold the bat, he will fly through the wheels without ever hitting a spoke. He has been able to do that for centuries.

Well, investigators have found that bats are using sonar radio, and that with it they even fly better blindfolded than when they can see. The bat puts out a sort of standardized beep. We humans can hear sound frequencies up to about fifteen thousand vibrations a second. The beep of the bat goes up to seventy-five or eighty thousand vibrations a second, and by hearing the reflection of that sound he recognizes an obstruction ahead and measures how big it is and how much he needs to turn out to avoid it.

Once when I was in England I was shown a high-speed motion picture of a falling cat. They had held this cat up with his feet upward and let him go, and he had turned over in the air and landed on his feet, as any intelligent cat would do. The interesting thing about it was that a mathematician had worked out differential equations for each position of the cat as he fell. "It is perfectly marvelous," he said, "the way those equations fit into each other."

"How would you expect them to fit?" I asked. "The cat landed on his feet, didn't he?"

"But how can a cat know this?" he exclaimed.

As nearly as I can understand from history, cats were turning over and landing on their feet long before differential equations were invented. The cat just feels the business of how to turn over as he falls, how to land on his feet, and he doesn't have to do any calculating at all. If he had to work out the differential equations for it, he wouldn't land on his feet but on his back or on his head, and there wouldn't be any cat.

So the more we fly the more we have respect for the way the birds do it. And the longer we run submarines the more respect we are going to have for the fish. We do not recognize that nature has set a little simple pattern out here and all we have to do is to go and study it and be willing to recognize that, whether it is the way we like it or not, it is correct.

When we talk about science triumphing over nature, we sometimes want to picture ourselves as the gala knight of old with his sword held high and with his foot on the dragon's head, representing the laws of nature. I don't like that picture at all, because I would sooner picture this thing as a humble worker who is thankful that he has had an opportunity to work with these things, thankful that he has had an opportunity to do something for his fellow men. And I cannot help but think that, as that fellow is being thankful, I can hear a little echo from the Great Intelligence saying, "Just in proportion as you recognize your ignorance, the road for greater knowledge will be opened."

We think we represent the population of the world. Now sometime I would like some scientist to find out what the real population of the world is. I mean by that, dogs, cats, bugs, bees, worms, and all the other creatures, ants, mosquitoes, the whole living outfit. Let him put the number down on paper and set the population of mankind beside it. I don't think you would notice the number of mankind, it would be so small. We are always complaining about some kind of bug spoiling our crops. But I'll bet that if that bug could publish a newspaper it would say how much trouble he had been having with another kind of animal taking his oats away.

The birds and the bees and the butterflies have just as much right here as we have. We have so "egotized" ourselves that we think we are going to tell the world how it is going to run from now on. We're not. Some fellow has figured out that if you had a box as big as a cubic mile—that is, a mile on each side—you could put in there every human being on the earth, pack them in like sardines, drop that in the ocean, and nobody could tell that you had done it. There are more than 300 million cubic miles of sea water, and just putting one more cubic mile in there—you couldn't find it. That's how important we are. The sun and the moon would come up as usual and nearly everything else would go along exactly the same.

I think that this whole question of providing food, providing everything, is still in the most primitive form. We don't know enough to grow anything for ten minutes. We don't know anything about the biological process. If you had to run your own body by having your heart, your kidneys, and everything else function the way they ought by what we know about them, five minutes would be your length of life. You might hang on for an hour, but that would be as far as you would go. We just don't know very much about these processes.

I rub my hands together. They get hot. I wonder why. You say that is simply on account of friction. Well, what is friction? About the only definition is that it is what makes our hands get warm when we rub them together. That is all we know about the most elementary thing in mechanics.

I once asked a famous scientist this question: "Why can I see through a pane of glass?"

"That's very simple," he said, "glass is transparent."

I'm afraid the word "transparent" means nothing to me at all. "You can see through a pane of glass because you can see through a pane of glass." That is what we say when we get through with it.

I would like to know *why* I can see through a pane of glass. It is a mystery and has been a mystery ever since I was a kid looking out the kitchen window. I would like to know whether light waves travel through the glass as light or whether they are received and rebroadcast in some other form from molecule to molecule.

We have been very smart in hiding our ignorance. A man in Kentucky years ago was able to say "I don't know" in the most classical and artistic way I have ever heard. We were in a section of Kentucky where at that time there were very few roads and we got lost. Soon we overtook a native of the place, and we asked him how to get to Cincinnati from there.

"Well," he replied, "You go up here to the forks. There you turn left. Let me see. No, I guess you'd better turn right. Well now, to tell you the truth, if I was goin' to Cincinnati, I just wouldn't start from here."

We are all in some such locality as that ourselves. If we are going to get out of here and make it a better world, we must arrive at the conclusion that wherever we go we start from here.

It is so easy to look back but so difficult to look ahead. That is why so many say, "We don't see much chance for improvement over what we have now." The reason for that, I think, is that we overemphasize, overestimate what we know. We don't know much and we are afraid to admit it. What we need to do is to recognize that there is so much we don't know—in fact, almost everything! So the big thing in the future is to substitute new facts for old opinions.

A friend of mine in one of the steel companies has always sent me a little sample of steel every time they got out a new one. I can remember when we first went into the automobile business steel had a tensile strength of about 80,000 pounds to the square inch, and that was about as far as we could go. Then it went up to 100,000, and that was the limit. After a while we got to 150,000, and everybody knew that was the limit.

So when my friend sent me a little piece of steel that had a tensile strength of 300,000 pounds to the square inch, I was very much interested. I took it to our analytical department and said, "I would like to have you analyze this to find out what its composition is."

The analyst took the sample to the machine shop to have some holes bored in it so he could have the chips to analyze. The man who tried to drill it came back and said, "I can't drill that piece of steel. It is too hard."

When later I asked about the results of the analysis, they said, "We could not get any chips to analyze because the piece is too hard to drill."

"Why do you say that?" I asked.

"Just come out here and we will show you." They put in a brand new drill and when it came down on that steel the edge of the drill just rolled over.

"But it's not that the steel is too hard," I said. "The drill is too soft. Did you try a diamond-pointed drill on it?" They put in a diamond drill and had no trouble getting the chips.

And there is the point exactly, we are all the time blaming difficulties on to something else. Our real trouble is that we are too soft to solve the problem. Take the doctors who talk about incurable diseases. The only incurable diseases are those the doctors don't know how to cure. That is the way with all problems. I don't believe the Lord ever put in his deck any "jokers" like incurable diseases.

Once during a visit to Tunis I heard this interesting story about the circumstance that so often people do not ask whether difficulties cannot be overcome. An intelligent but young traveler was going through an Eastern country when unintentionally he offended one of the sacred rites of the religion of the people. With a great deal of formality he was tried and condemned by a group of religious leaders. He was sentenced to jump off a certain cliff at a specified number of days hence. To impress upon the young man the seriousness of the sentence, he was imprisoned on the very cliff from which he was to jump so he could look down into the rocky gorge below.

Every morning, noon, and night a kindly old priest came to him and said: "My son, do you appreciate the full significance of your sentence?"

"Yes," he replied.

And the priest said, "Repeat it to me." As time passed the young man became more depressed, and the old priest said: "I am sorry, my son, you do not yet comprehend the full significance of your sentence." And he would have him repeat it over and over again.

About two days before the sentence was to have been carried out, when the priest came he asked once more, "Do you fully comprehend the significance of your sentence?"

And the young man replied, "Yes, *now* I do. Do you think it would be possible for me to buy ten tons of hay and have it put down in the gorge below?"

And the priest said, "My son, your intelligence has overcome your fear."

The sentence did not say on what he had to land, you see. It only said he was going to have to jump.

So we take ourselves too seriously, that is what is wrong with us. We forget that we are just transients in the long progression of our particular species of biology and that our mistakes may be the great successes of the next generation.

I have often said that the human race is the great experiment of the Lord. Perhaps He thought, "I am going to give one of these animals of mine an intelligence and I am going to see whether with intelligence and the ability to think he perfects himself or destroys himself."

Most people think and talk as though the creation of mankind was the final finishing touch of Creation and that that represents the highest form of the work of the Creator. But my contention is that the only real experiment the Lord has ever tried was when He created man. Up to the present time, man's record is pretty much against him. Intelligence has built up selfishness and egotism. We believe this whole universe was built entirely for us. The greatest battle the human race has before it is whether human intelligence is going to overbalance jealousy and egotism or not.

RESEARCH AND SOCIAL PROGRESS

Although Kettering's major activity was in the fields of science and engineering, he had a vital interest in people and concern about them.

It was human progress that he tried to promote. In this he believed that there is no terminal point.

L OUDONVILLE, OHIO, NEAR WHICH I WAS REARED, IS A TOWN OF about 2,500 people. It is the trading center of a prosperous farming community. Thousands of such places make up rural America. What has transpired there is typical of what has happened everywhere, for we must remember that every city was once a small town. The development of this community is an example of what agriculture, industry, and labor, in cooperation with science, engineering, and management, can produce.

As a farm boy I attended the high school there and can remember what the town was like fifty years ago [1]—no paved streets in town, and only dirt roads in the country, at times just streaks in the deep mud. We had no modern conveniences. For instance, people were dependent for their water supply on wells located in the streets or back yards. There were two means of transportation: horse and buggy, and the railroad. You could always walk, of course. Our communications consisted of the telegraph at the depot and *one* telephone in a drugstore.

After graduating from high school when I was teaching in a district school about five miles from Loudonville, an incident occurred which shows some of the thinking of that time. For one day only, Friday, a railroad car of the California Land and Fruit Growers Association was exhibited in Loudonville at the depot siding to stimulate interest in California as a new place to live and prosper. The car must have been a great success if it was responsible in even a small way for California's great development.

---

[1] Said in 1944.

As an added attraction in the car, they had one of the very early X-ray machines. So Friday afternoon at recess, I dismissed the school and walked to the depot with the older boys and girls. The pupils had a wonderful time with the X-rays, looking at the bones in their hands and the nails in their shoes. I believe every one of them learned much from the experience.

On the following Sunday after church, the minister called one of the school directors aside and in a disturbed voice said, "I understand that the teacher dismissed school and walked down to see that California exhibit without your permission. That was bad enough," he continued, "but why did he show the boys and girls that infernal machine they call an X-ray? You know it must be the work of the evil spirit because if human eyes were intended to see through boards, nature would have given them that power."

That was less than fifty years ago. Today doctors everywhere are constantly using that "infernal machine" and many other similar scientific devices in their successful fight against disease. And the X-ray is an everyday tool in industry even to internally examining slabs of steel a foot or more thick.

As I look down Main Street in Loudonville today, I see many automobiles parked where the hitching rails used to be. Over there is a motion picture theater and nearly every home and farm has a telephone and electricity. Large airplanes pass overhead and the smaller ones can land there. A thousand radios bring the best in music and entertainment. The farmers in the neighborhood have up-to-date equipment and they ride on fine highways. In town there are new schools, paved streets, sewers, waterworks, natural gas and all the other things that have followed in the wake of the automobile and electric power.

As technologists we do not want to set our field apart; we want to be servants of humanity. But since technology is related cold-bloodedly to mechanical pursuits or materialistic things, it is often distinguished from cultural pursuits. We inventors and engineers do not think that there is any differentiation at all. We think that these technological and scientific advances are mediums for spreading culture. Because of the marvelous distribution system that we have through radio, people at the fishing camps today hear more music than you could hear in the greatest palace of music in the world a few years ago. In a short time, you will actually see events by means of radar and television.[2] These are only mediums through which you are able to do the things that you would like to do, and do more of them in less time.

A young fellow, a graduate of one of our large universities, was talking to me about the social significances of these technological developments. "The great trouble with America," he said, "is that we are technically so far ahead that we cannot catch up socially. We can't adjust ourselves. You have developed too fast and therefore there ought to be a law to prevent any invention from being made for the next ten years."

I told him that I had not noticed the strain. I guess that is because I was born and raised on a farm. "Let's test this social strain business," I said. "I would like to get it straight."

We were in the bookstore where he worked and I said, "You have a warehouse, I presume. Take up that telephone and call the warehouse and order these books. Does that put any strain on you, or would you sooner walk to the warehouse and get the books?" He said he would rather use the telephone.

"Take up that telephone receiver and say you would like to speak to the Savoy Hotel in London," I said. "In a couple of minutes they will be on the wire. I don't think that is going to put you to any social strain. The only question is whether you have anything worth saying that far away from home or not. That is the main thing."

All I have to say to those who claim things have gone too far is to take your pencil and put an X-mark at the place where you think developments should have stopped and go back there and try it

---

[2] Spoken in 1948 at the seventy-fifth anniversary of The Ohio State University. Earlier, in 1934, at a symposium on "Science and Industry in the Coming Century," Kettering had said, "We can have television and an unapproached number of other things."

out for a few days; and, if you think things there are all right, come and tell me.

Supposing you got a strep infection, would you like to be back ten years ago? Sulfanilamide has made a wonderful difference in strep infections and it's less than ten years old.[3] How far back do you want to go in any of the things that you know today? You don't want to go back one day.

There is a story about the fellow who went to the railroad station to take the ten o'clock train. He got there at nine-thirty, but the train had already gone. So he sued the railroad company for letting the train pull out ahead of time. But in the trial the railroad company proved that the train did not leave ahead of schedule. It was the train of the day before, 23 hours and 30 minutes late.

Well, that is exactly our situation technologically, we are not ahead. We are a lap or more behind.

When I was on the radio program of General Motors [4] I used to get many letters. One of these received about the time our armies were fighting around Metz, France, in World War II, said: "If you would wash out of the universe all the scientific laboratories, we would have no more war." That seemed very simple. But I looked up the history of Metz and found that battles were being fought at Metz 1,400 years before the discovery of America. So I just had a little of that history photostated, sent it to the writer of that letter, and asked, "How do you account for this?" But I never got a reply.

As a long-time inventor, I was called before a number of committees concerned with the implications of inventions. One of these was contending that if a person was going to invent things he should have to be responsible, too, for the social implications of his inventions. I said to them that I'd be willing to accept responsibility for the social implications of my inventions, if the committee promised that no one would ever use them for things they were not

---

[3] Said in 1946.
[4] General Motors Symphony of the Air, National Broadcasting Company, September, 1943, to July, 1946.

invented for. I'll take my responsibility and you take yours, I said.

Let me tell you what I had in mind. After the first World War I had some men searching for a new refrigerant. Ammonia was the compound in common use then. We also had sulfur dioxide, and both were very bad-smelling and nauseating. We recognized that as long as you had nauseating or dangerous refrigerants it would seriously limit what could be done in air conditioning.

So we set up an objective like this: We were after a refrigerant that would be nontoxic and noninflammable. We were out to get a refrigerant that wouldn't hurt anyone if you threw a bucketful of it on the floor.

When we tried to solve that problem, compounds containing fluorine always got into the picture as the only possible solution. But a little learning is a dangerous thing, for everybody knew at that time that fluorine had none of the properties named. They said, "My God, you wouldn't try to use fluorine, because hydrofluoric acid will eat up glass, let alone metal!" So I said, "You ought to give it a chance to prove it."

Well, out of this effort came an entirely new compound which worked beautifully and which has proved to be the best tailor-made refrigerant in the world. In other words, it is one of the nicest, most accommodating of gases. This is the fluorine-containing compound which was named "Freon."

As the result of the discovery of this new refrigerant, all risk of toxic harm was removed from home or hospital refrigeration and air conditioning. No longer need people worry about the refrigerator leaking, or the gas injuring those who might be sleeping.

But during World War II you could not get that new compound for use as a refrigerant. And why couldn't you get it for that use? Because Freon proved to be the best solvent for pyrethrum and other insect-controlling compounds in those aerosol bombs, which were used as a most effective weapon against malaria-bearing mosquitoes on the battlefront. Thus this tailor-made refrigerant was asked to do an entirely new job that was not even remotely considered in the original specification.

Freon was also found to be the best insulator for electrical machinery under certain peculiar conditions. So here two entirely unsuspected uses for it came into being—things we never had in mind when we made it.

No one can sit in judgment of any newborn idea and say what its future uses may be. So you can implicate me as an inventor only insofar as I am conscious of what I am doing. I will take the social implications of having invented a good refrigerant if the other inventors will take their responsibilities.

That mathematician who first gave to mankind the knowledge that two and two equal four was revealing a fundamental truth. If others distort that truth, that is not his fault. Let us not, for God's sake, condemn a principle because somebody misuses it. If that were the case, we would quit making motorcars because some man used one to rob a bank.

The only trouble with the world is people. But it would be mighty lonesome if they weren't here. The whole difficulty is the fact that we are human beings. I would rather work with the human being, even with his peculiarities and everything else, and be associated with folks, than to be out on a desert island by myself.

I get the greatest "kick" out of talking with new people, no matter whether they are ditch-diggers or bankers. The man who can give me a new slant on things is always interesting, and I like to talk with him. To learn a new thing gives me the fullest satisfaction. That is the reason I am so much in love with my job as a research man.

There are two kinds of information in the world—information about things and information about people. Now, I have been an inventor all my life and I have worked with things. Things are much more reasonable than people and they don't change their opinions nearly as much as people do. You can work on a thing today; and, if it works a certain way today, it will work the same way tomorrow.

If some of the people who are interested in social, economic, or governmental improvement would like to try some of the methods used by the scientists, I am sure we would all lend a hand. We know two things: first, research requires a great patience and, second, it takes a lot of time. Both are important in the development of anything worth while, whether it is a new product or a new form of government.

Everyone knows that if a manufacturer puts into production the ideas of an unknown inventor without proper tests, the company would surely go broke. Yet that is exactly what was done in Germany, when the Nazis put their ideologies into force. A man without any background whatever in government, finance, or business, presented an idea which, through his political influence and the nature of the economy in the country at the time, was put into operation over the whole of Germany. Out of this act came the destruction of the country and serious injury to the whole world.

The desire to rush untried ideas into government is nothing new. History is full of such attempts. A knowledge of this trend was, no doubt, the reason why the framers of our Constitution went to such great lengths to guard against our picking up some untried or impractical ideas and quickly making them a part of our national law and government. We have a lot of people revolutionizing the world because they never had to present a working model.

I go to Loudonville quite often. With the old neighbors and friends we sit around and talk. One of these friends said to me, "Charlie, I believe in this 'One World' idea. Why don't you try to do something about it?"

"Jim," I replied, "I think you are right. But why don't we make this little town the center of this One World? Everything has to start somewhere. Why don't we start it right here? This is a town of about 2,500 people and we have six Protestant churches and a Catholic church. I'll tell you what we'll do. Let us start this One World by getting those six Protestant churches all together into one. I will put up the money to build the church, and we'll put a fine pipe organ in it. We will have a really wonderful institution. And that will start off the One World idea."

Then Jim said to me, "Charlie, you know you could never get all those churches to go together into one!"

"Well," I said, "if you can't get those six churches to unite, what are you going to do about your One World? Maybe we can have this One World, but I don't think we are going to get it by Saturday evening. You can't make the human race over, for it might be worse than it is now."

I have always been a great student of bugs, and I have learned an awful lot about human beings by studying them. People go out to the Grand Canyon to look at that wonderful work of nature, or they go to Switzerland to view the Alps. "Wonderful, it is wonderful!" they say. Yet the simplest bug running around on the front porch has those wonders backed off the map. There is an organism in the bug, while the Grand Canyon and the Alps are simply where things didn't match up, a sort of wreck. So these same people will step on the bug and kill it, saying, "Now, you nasty thing, you are gone."

A friend of mine sent me a picture of a wasp which he had taken in some of the excavations around Pompeii, Italy. He knew that I was interested in wasps, and this particular picture was of the ancient nest of a hunting wasp as it had been opened up. It had been there a long while.

The hunting wasp is a solitary creature, living in the ground, and it preys upon crickets. Its method is to catch three crickets and sting them in the motor nerve centers. It does not kill them. It only paralyzes them. The three crickets are then dragged into the underground nest of the wasp and laid on their backs. Next, the wasp lays her egg on the middle cricket, always at exactly the same place, so that when the egg hatches and the little grub emerges its mouth comes right at the tenderest spot on the middle cricket. It eats the three crickets, converts the meat into silk and spins around itself a cocoon which lies there until the following May or June.

Then, enlivened by the radiation from the sun, it chews its way out of the cocoon and is another hunting wasp. It has no education. There is no educational system in the wasp library, because all the parents disappeared in the frost of the previous fall. But it proceeds to act exactly according to the routine stored up in the egg which its mother laid. It goes through precisely the same performance as did the one taken from the ruins of Pompeii. It goes out, meets up with a partner, digs the same kind of hole, catches the same kind of crickets, stings them in exactly the same place, and lays an egg in precisely the same spot. The cycle never changes, never improves.

That is true of almost every living organism, with the exception of the human race. Mankind is the only one that has been given the possibilities of utilizing all of the great phenomena of nature—to do things independently, to break hereditary strain. Instead of merely adapting himself to his environment, as has been true of almost all other organisms, the human being has said, "I am going to make my environment suit me." He started in to do that. He began to build houses, to cultivate the fields, to raise animals and beasts of burden. He began to make marks in caves and ultimately to write books and to put on record what he had done.

But even among us humans there are an awful lot of wasps. We run along in the same old track and do the same old things. Everybody gets into a rut, everybody wants a milk route. Just try to do something new and you will find out how much of the "wasp" is still sticking in.

We humans are almost the lowest form of animal parasite. There are lots of dumb animals that prey upon other animals, but they are limited in their choice of victims and they have no other means at their command. But we prey upon all animals, and that in spite of the fact that we have enough brains to provide for ourselves. We play no favorites when we start out to kill and steal.

We are nest robbers. We steal the eggs from the chicken and, to make it worse, we use our science to make her lay more eggs so that we can commit grand instead of petty larceny on her product. And, after we have stolen hundreds of her eggs, we cut off her head and eat her too.

A lady friend of mine once told me that that day she had gotten her husband to shoot a cat because it had eaten a bird. But I like cats and I couldn't help feeling sorry for the poor cat. Some time later I was dining with this lady and her husband and she ordered quail on toast. I said to her husband, "Here is another job for your gun. You should shoot your wife for doing what the cat did."

The silkworm spins a cocoon to clothe herself, and we rip her garment from her and make it into one for ourselves. The cotton fiber is primarily a little parachute with which to float the cotton-seed away in order to scatter it. We are just learning to get out of the by-product class. By this I mean that we are learning that a thing has got to be made specifically for a definite purpose. Anybody who will stop to think for a minute knows that an egg and a piece of bacon were never designed primarily for food. Now, someday we are going to make from primary materials such foods and fibers as are necessary for us.[5]

I think one great difficulty is that we sometimes worry ourselves about idealism and forget that we have to live in realism. That's why I don't worry very much. Every minute I worry I am not doing something else and that tears down the system. We have these problems in front of us. We have to face them in the best way we possibly can. We can't go back and change history.

I used to go to a country school near an old mill—one of those old stone gristmills which were used before the roller process was developed. This mill was run by Isaac Wolf. Uncle Ike, as we called him, was more or less of a philosopher. He had the reputation of having to dress those millstones the fewest number of times of any miller in the country, considering the amount of grist he ground. And someone asked Uncle Ike why that was.

"You see that peck measure sitting there on the hopper?" he said. "I never allow that mill to turn unless there is grain in it. And when a customer's grist is all ground, I throw in a peck of my own so that the stones never touch each other while I am stopping the mill.

---

[5] Said in 1926.

"Do you know that people are a good bit like that?" he continued. "If you run this mill without any grist in it, the stones rub together and you just dull them. Soon the mill must be shut down while you redress the stones. When you are worrying about things you can't do anything about, you are just running your mill without any grist in it."

Our civilization as a whole is new. This is the first time in the history of the world that such a civilization has been in existence. It in itself is an experiment, and just because we have encountered difficulty is no cause for despair. We must find out what is wrong and then remedy it, but we must not give up hope of a better and more secure life.[6]

We have in the United States a simple, fundamental principle of deciding things by votes. Some call it capitalism, and speak of capitalism as opposed to communism. I think this leads to confusion in thought. It is communism versus human liberty. It is communism versus the right to own property, to own a home, to think the way you want to think, to talk the way you want to talk, to belong to the church you want to join. These are the things that are at stake. It is not merely capitalism, for those are the things that make up capitalism. The minute you own anything you are a capitalist. So let's talk about communism versus the right to own a home, to own an automobile, or for that matter to own anything at all.

We have a Constitution and we believe in constitutional government. We also believe in constitutional rights; but I don't think anybody has any constitutional rights who is trying to use them in order to destroy the Constitution itself. I do not believe that anyone has the right to free speech who is trying, by the use of that free speech, to destroy free speech.

Since I have retired I have organized a couple of new companies. The first I have named the Utopian Transportation Company, Limited. This is a nonprofit organization to give free transportation. Its purpose is to give free travel tickets to those who get up in

---

[6] Said in 1934, during the depression prevailing then.

the public square and tell you that this is a "lousy" country. It would give them travel tickets to where they want to go—not where you want them to go, but where they want to go. This company is called the Utopian Transportation Company, Limited—limited to furnishing transportation in one direction only.

The other new company I have organized to sell stock—stock in the greatest corporation the world has ever seen. This company I have called United States Preferred.

I see many, many problems in front of our country. But, after we add up where we stand with the rest of the world, I think our problem of the future is to perfect what we have and not discard it in favor of some untried or theoretical systems that have to date nothing to show for their claims.

Much that science will discover is yet to come to the farms, towns, and cities of America. Much is already here. We should analyze the process which has produced such amazing progress in such a short time and make sure it continues. If there is anything wrong with the system, let's fix it, and not unintelligently or willfully destroy it.

So I want everyone to buy one, or a hundred thousand shares of United States Preferred. Let's keep this the greatest nation that God ever let rest on the face of the earth.

APPENDIX

I

SHORT BIOGRAPHY OF CHARLES F. KETTERING [1]

Charles Franklin Kettering, son of Jacob and Martha (Hunter) Kettering, was born on a farm near Loudonville, Ohio, August 29, 1876. That was the year in which the telephone was invented and in which the great Exhibition in Philadelphia celebrated the completion of a century since the Declaration of Independence. Charlie Kettering's early life on the farm was no different from that of other country boys, except as his turn of mind made it different.

He went to the one-room country school and later, with an apple in his pocket, walked three miles back and forth each day to the high school in Loudonville. Then he became a country schoolteacher and Friday night debater. In 1898, at age twenty-two, he went to The Ohio State University to study electrical engineering, but early in his sophomore year trouble with his eyes forced him to leave the university. In the two years following he worked for the Star Telephone Company in the small city of Ashland, Ohio. There he began work digging holes for telephone poles, but during his stay he learned to do everything in the operation of the system and also made some improvements in it.

In the fall of 1901 Kettering returned to the university to see whether his still weak eyes would let him finish the course. Saving his eyes, he did not study books as much as the other students. He often lay on his back on the bed and listened to his classmates read the assignments. Later he joked that he could always tell how much studying he had done at night by how hoarse his roommate was in the morning. But it was luck, he said too, that thus forced him to work things out in his head. It sharpened his imagination.

In 1904 Kettering graduated from Ohio State at the late age of twenty-eight. He fully expected to go back into the telephone busi-

---

[1] For a more comprehensive life story see the book, *Professional Amateur, The Biography of Charles Franklin Kettering,* by T. A. Boyd, E. P. Dutton and Company, 1957.

ness, but he was offered an attractive opportunity to become an experimental engineer at the National Cash Register Company in Dayton, Ohio, which he accepted instead. In five years there, he utilized electricity to take the tiresome hand crank off the cash register, developed a low-cost printing register and a combined telephone and cash register credit system for department stores, as well as one of the first accounting machines for banks.

After having invented meanwhile a better ignition system for automobiles, Kettering resigned from the National Cash Register Company in 1909 and became an independent inventor and development engineer. With Edward A. Deeds, an executive of the National Cash Register Company and the man who had induced him to join the staff of that concern, he organized for that purpose the Dayton Engineering Laboratories Company, which began its modest operations in what had been the hayloft of the Deedses' barn.

Soon Kettering made that historic development, the electric self-starter for automobiles, which appeared on the 1912 model Cadillac. This was the device which so greatly enlarged the usefulness of the motorcar, and which made it possible for women to drive.

But the application of the self-starter forced the Dayton Engineering Laboratories Company—Delco, for short—to become a manufacturing concern, much against the wishes of its organizers. And before long they were operating a factory employing 1,200 persons.

Nevertheless, Kettering found time to continue his experimentation. Soon he developed an engine-driven unit to furnish electric light and power on farms. This development and his prior work on battery ignition for automobiles led him into another field in which he became the principal pioneer. This was the field of automobile fuels in which he made a long and productive effort to overcome their principal defect—the distressing bugbear of knock which limits the compression and therefore both the power and the efficiency of engines.

To work on that problem and others, he organized a new laboratory in a second attempt to free his research from the hindrances always present in a manufacturing concern. World War I came just at that time, and out of wartime activities in that new laboratory came the first synthetic high-octane aviation gasoline and a manless automatic bombing plane which was the predecessor of the guided missile.

Soon after World War I, Kettering accepted an insistent invitation to organize and direct a central research laboratory for General Motors Corporation. He organized that laboratory around the small one he had set up just a few years before, and for the twenty-seven years following he served as vice president and head of research for General Motors. He was also made a member of the Board of Directors of General Motors.

The developments which came out of Kettering's activities in those years were far too many to be enumerated here. But among them were the discovery of tetraethyl lead as an antiknock agent, which compound has since been used in nearly all automobile and aviation gasolines, and the searching out of basic knowledge about the relationship of hydrocarbon structure to behavior in combustion. Together, these two advances opened the way to high-octane gasolines and high compression in engines. A few of the many other advances made during Kettering's years with General Motors were the development of better and longer-lasting finishes for automobiles, the discovery of the nontoxic and noninflammable fluorocarbons as refrigerants, the finding of means to take out of engines the old-time shake and shiver which were so distressing to automobile drivers and which cut down the utility and durability of cars, and the development of an improved diesel engine which, in one of its several applications, sparked a revolution in the powering of railroads.

But Kettering's influence in the success of General Motors went far beyond the contributions he made through his research endeavors. Shortly before Kettering retired in 1947, Alfred P. Sloan, Jr., then Chairman of the Board, said this: "Mr. Kettering's contribution to General Motors has been most outstanding. . . . That contribution divides itself into the tangibles and the intangibles. . . . I would say that the intangible side of it, if it could be evaluated, has meant more to all of us than all the tangible things, important as they are. He has been an inspiration to me and to the whole organization, particularly in directing our thoughts and our imagination and our activities toward doing a better job technically and the tremendous importance of technological progress."

On his own account, through the Charles F. Kettering Foundation, which he established in 1927 to search out new knowledge for the benefit of mankind, Kettering instituted and for years pursued a fundamental search for a better and more efficient way to utilize the tremendous energy of sunshine. It was his purpose to aid in finding a more effective and efficient means for capturing the energy the sun sends us so lavishly—a means by which that energy could be made available in the greatest abundance to people everywhere, whether as food or as fuel.

He spent many years, too, in search of an answer to the question: What is magnetism? a mystery which had fascinated him throughout his career.

Also, through research at Washington University, at the Sloan-Kettering Institute for Cancer Research, and at the Southern Research Institute, he did what he could to aid in the search for ways to prevent and cure cancer. That dread disease struck especially hard in his own family. It snatched Mrs. Kettering from him in 1946, and at other times his two sisters.

After Kettering retired in 1947, he remained active in the field of research, devoting most of his time to the three endeavors just named—solar energy, magnetism, and cancer. During that time he did much laboratory experimentation of his own on the first two of those three subjects.

With Kettering, as with others consecrated to it, the search for new knowledge was a religion. Dr. C. P. Rhoads, the first director of the Sloan-Kettering Institute for Cancer Research, said this about Kettering's views of research: "His principal point is that if one is to have a productive career in research, one must have some well-defined objective. . . . Without objectives, he feels, scientific life is unsatisfactory and scientific work in general unproductive. This point of view is, of course, in sharp contrast to that so frequently enunciated in recent years by those who believe sincerely that there should be no objective in research." But Kettering believed that research not aimed at contributing in some way to human needs is not justified.

Popular as a public speaker, Kettering made hundreds of addresses and radio speeches. These were full of the wit and wisdom characteristic of him. Many of his sayings have been widely quoted. Most of these are included in the body of this work and fifty of them are collected in Part III of the Appendix. One of the biggest contributions Kettering made to progress was as a vocal advocate of revitalizing changes in industry, not in his own company alone but in others as well.

Some aid to understanding why it was that Kettering was able to do so much creative work is given by the evaluations placed upon him by two of the nation's eminent men. The great scientist, Robert A. Millikan, said of Kettering that he was unique in that "he combines in one individual the interest in pure science with the practical ability to apply knowledge in useful devices." Willis R. Whitney, long head of research for the General Electric Company, said of Kettering: "We have never had another man like him in America. He is the most willing man to do things I have ever seen. Benjamin Franklin was a little like him. Both had horse sense and love of fun. If a fellow goes to school long enough he gets frozen in his thinking. He is not free any more. But Ket has always been free."

Kettering was generous with his time outside his principal field of endeavor. Among a multitude of such activities, some of which are enumerated in Part II of this Appendix, were his services as president of the American Association for the Advancement of Science in 1945 and of the Society of Automotive Engineers in 1918, and as chairman of the National Inventors Council from the time of its formation in 1940. From his contemporaries he received a host of distinctions, many of which also are named in Part II of this Appendix.

In 1905 Kettering married Olive Williams, of whom he said that she was a perfect supplement to an absent-minded inventor. They had one son, Eugene W., who now, as president of the Charles F. Kettering Foundation, is trying to carry forward some of the scientific and humanitarian endeavors begun by his father and to extend his influence in other ways. Mrs. Kettering died in 1946, and afterwards Kettering said of her that she was the only possession of his he had never tried to improve. Kettering died on November 25, 1958, leaving behind him a vast heritage to the people of the nation from a dynamic, many-sided, and highly creative life.

II

Partial Listing of the
DISTINCTIONS KETTERING RECEIVED FROM HIS CONTEMPORARIES

HONORARY DEGREES

Doctor of Science

1928   University of Cincinnati
1932   Brown University
1934   Toledo University (Ohio)
1935   Northwestern University
1936   Lafayette College
1937   New York University
1939   Dartmouth College
1939   Harvard University
1942   Otterbein College
1943   Columbia University
1945   Syracuse University
1945   Oberlin College
1947   University of Miami (Florida)
1947   Washington University
1949   University of Alabama
1950   New York State Board of Regents
1953   University of Florida
1954   Butler University
1955   Wilmington College
1958   Bradley University

Doctor of Engineering

1929   The Ohio State University
1929   University of Michigan
1930   Polytechnic Institute of Brooklyn
1934   University of Detroit
1954   Worcester Polytechnic Institute
1956   Indiana Technical College

Doctor of Laws

1943   Antioch College
1945   Temple University
1947   Princeton University
1949   Lehigh University
1956   Wabash College
1957   Kenyon College

Other Honorary Degrees

1941   Honorary Fellow, Stanford University
1943   Doctor of Engineering Research, University of Nebraska
1946   Doctor of Humanities, Wayne State University
1947   Doctor of Humane Letters, College of Wooster
1952   Doctor of Humanities, University of Dayton
1952   Civil Engineer, Rensselaer Polytechnic Institute

AWARDS, CITATIONS, AND MEDALS

1922   Hall of Fame, Aeronautical Association of America
1929   Sullivant Medal, The Ohio State University
1930   Medal in Tribute, University of Cincinnati
1930   Benefactor of Dayton, Medallion, Dayton Civitan Club
1936   Washington Award, Western Society of Engineers and Four
        Founders Societies, ASCE, ASME, AIEE, and AIMME,
        "On account of accomplishments which preeminently pro-
        mote the happiness, comfort, and well-being of humanity."
1936   John Scott Memorial Award, Board of City trusts of Phila-
        delphia
1936   Franklin Gold Medal, The Franklin Institute
1937   Legion of Honor of France (Chevalier)
1937   Medal, American Club of Paris
1938   Officer of the Order of the Crown, Belgium
1938   Order of LaCouronne, France
1940   Gold Key, American Congress of Physical Therapy
1940   Medal, American Society of Mechanical Engineers, "For
        outstanding inventions and research."
1940   Modern Pioneers Award, American Manufacturers Associ-
        ation

1943 Certificate for William Park Woodside Lecture, Detroit Chapter, American Society for Metals

1944 John Fritz Medal, the four Founders Societies, ASCE, ASME, AIEE, and AIMME, "For notable achievements in the field of industrial research which have contributed greatly to the welfare of mankind and of the nation."

1945 Thomas A. Edison Award, Society of Arts and Sciences

1946 Certificate for Andrew R. Biddle Oration, Michigan State Medical Society

1946 Tribute from the Citizens of Loudonville, Ohio, at Civic Celebration of C.F.K.'s seventieth birthday

1947 Silver Beaver Award, Boy Scouts of America, "For distinguished service to boyhood."

1947 Distinguished Health Service Award, Michigan State Medical Society

1948 Alumnus of the Year, American Alumni Council, "As one whose life and work will be honored for all time as exemplifying the college-trained man at his noblest and best."

1948 Gold Medal for Distinguished Achievement, American Petroleum Institute

1948 Certificate of Schwab Memorial Lecture, American Iron and Steel Institute

1948 Citation, National Federation of Sales Executives and the Sales Executives Club of New York, "For outstanding accomplishments as a salesman and scientist whose philosophy and example have been a source of inspiration to all in the profession of selling."

1948 Distinguished Service Citation, Automobile Old Timers

1949 Citizenship Award, Ohio State Bar Association

1949 Gold Medal, International Benjamin Franklin Society

1950 Governor's Award, Ohio Newspaper Association

1950 Certificate of Appreciation, Ohio Society of Professional Engineers

1950 Award for Achievement, Advertising Club of New York

1950 Science Award, Ohioana Library Association

1950 Silver Buffalo Award, Boy Scouts of America

1951 Centennial Award, Northwestern University

1952 Horatio Alger Award, American Schools and Colleges, for enhancing "The American tradition of overcoming obstacles to achieve success."

1952 Jefferson Medal, New Jersey Patent Law Association

1953 Award for 1953, National Society of Professional Engineers

1953   Gold Medal for Distinguished Service to Humanity, National Institute of Social Sciences

1954   Engineer of the Year, National Association of Power Engineers

1954   Knight of the Round Table, National Management Association

1955   Hoover Medal, American Society of Mechanical Engineers, "For great, unselfish, nontechnical services by engineers to their fellow men."

1955   Silver Quill Award, National Business Publications

1956   Certificate, American Medical Association, on behalf of his "lifelong enthusiasm and ingenuity in charting new courses in medical research."

1956   Charles Franklin Kettering Award (the first) sponsored by six engineering societies, ASCE, ASME, AIEE, SAE, AIChE, AIMME

1956   Testimonial Plaque, Illinois Manufacturers Association

1957   Harry E. Salzberg Medal, Syracuse University

1958   Great Living American Award, United States Chamber of Commerce, "For contributions to the nation's industrial progress."

1958   Edison Medal (posthumous), American Institute of Electrical Engineers

Honorary and Life Memberships

1903   Society of Sigma Xi, Omega Chapter, The Ohio State University

1923   The Engineers' Club of Dayton, Honorary Life President

1927   American Society of Steel Treating Engineers

1928   National Academy of Sciences of the United States of America

1930   American Philosophical Society

1935   Society of Automotive Engineers

1936   National Geographic Society

1936   The Franklin Institute

1939   International College of Dentists

1944   Tau Beta Pi, The Ohio State University

1947   Southern Research Institute

1948   American Hospital Association

1949   American Society of Lubrication Engineers

1950   The Engineering Society of Cincinnati

1952 Academy of Political Science
1954 National Association of Power Engineers
1956 Horseless Carriage Club of America
1956 American Society of Heating and Air Conditioning Engineers

    Automobile Old Timers
    Dayton Junior Chamber of Commerce
    Dayton Bicycle Club
    Ohioana Library Association
    Rotary Club of Dayton

PRINCIPAL DIRECTORSHIPS AND TRUSTEESHIPS
(as of 1958)

Automoblie Old Timers	*Director*
Antioch College	*Trustee*
Committee of One Hundred (Miami Beach)	*President*
Ethyl Corporation (founder and first president)	*Director*
Thomas Alva Edison Foundation	*President*
Engineers' Club of Dayton	*Hon. President*
Fairchild Tropical Garden (Florida)	*Member Board Managers*
Flxible Company	*Chairman of Board*
General Motors Corporation	*Director*
Junior Achievement of Dayton	*Director*
C. F. Kettering, Incorporated	*Chairman of Board*
The Charles F. Kettering Foundation	*Vice President and Trustee*
Mead Corporation	*Director*
Miami Valley Hospital, Dayton	*Honorary President*
Montgomery County Airport, Dayton	*President*
National Cash Register Company	*Director*
National Geographic Society	*Trustee*
National Inventors Council	*Chairman*
The Ohio State University	*Trustee*
Patent, Trade-Mark and Copyright Foundation of George Washington University	*Member Advisory Council*
Sloan-Kettering Institute for Cancer Research	*Director*

III

FIFTY MAXIMS FROM THE SPEECHES OF
CHARLES F. KETTERING

I can conceive of nothing more foolish than to say the world is finished.

Your world, young men and young women, will be the kind of world you want it to be.

The opportunities of man are limited only by his imagination. But so few have imagination that there are ten thousand fiddlers to one composer.

What I believe is that, by proper effort, we can make the future almost anything we want to make it.

You can't have a better tomorrow if you are thinking about yesterday all the time.

Don't think some fellow is trying to pull you down. You can always get a good sight of your enemy in the morning when you shave.

You can go ahead and solve that difficulty if you don't get tired too quickly. Most people tire out after they try a thing the first time.

It doesn't matter if you try and try and try again, and fail. It does matter if you try and fail, and fail to try again.

It is the "follow-through" that makes the great difference between ultimate success and failure, because it is so easy to stop.

You must learn how to fail intelligently, for failing is one of the greatest arts in the world.

If you do not climb on top of your failures you will never get up to where you can have success.

Failures, *repeated* failures, are finger posts on the road to achievement. One *fails forward* toward success.

The only time you don't want to fail is the last time you try.

We think we are further along the path of knowledge than we actually are.

We have only begun to knock a few chips from the great quarry of knowledge that has been given us to dig out and use.

Just in proportion as you recognize your ignorance, the road for greater knowledge will be opened.

Some technical reports are so dry and dusty that if you put a pile of them in a hydraulic press and apply millions of pounds pressure to it, not a drop of juice will run out.

We find in research that a certain amount of intelligent ignorance is essential to human progress, because if you know too much you won't try the thing.

You can be sincere and still be stupid.

We should not be either ashamed or afraid to make intelligent mistakes. The greatest mistake of all is to do nothing.

Argument is always the indication of a lack of knowledge; and when two fellows argue either one of them is right and the other is wrong, or they are both part right and part wrong, or both of them are wrong—and it is usually the latter.

The only incurable diseases are those the doctors don't know how to cure.

Self-satisfaction is one of the world's worst diseases.

There is nothing permanent but change.

So long as we have younger generations we will have changes. Their views are new, their tastes are new, their likes are new—and emphatic.

There are lots of folks with oxcart minds riding around in automobiles.

The Wright brothers flew right through that smoke screen of impossibility.

Prejudice and precedent are the two watchdogs at the door of progress.

You can send a message around the world in one-seventh of a second, but it may take years for it to get from the outside of a man's head to the inside.

The price of progress is trouble, and I don't think the price is too high.

All human development must be outside the rules. Otherwise, we would never have anything new

Advancing waves of other people's progress sweep over the unchanging man and wash him out.

It is hard to pick out the balance wheel and the hairspring of a problem.

A problem is not solved in a laboratory. It is solved in some fellow's head, and all the apparatus is for is to get his head turned around so he can see the thing right.

You have to be "sold" on research before you can hope to get anywhere in it.

Research is something which if you don't undertake until you have to, it is too late.

Industries are like some watches—they have to be shaken hard every so often to keep them going.

Engineering must partake as much of economic horse sense as it does of scientific principles.

Engineering is a combination of brains and material, the more brains the less material.

The best engines are always the paper engines—the ones that have not yet been built.

When a fellow learns a new language he still speaks with the accent of the old.

Whenever anyone speaks of conquering nature, what he really means is that he has gotten right down on his knees and done exactly what nature wanted done under the circumstances.

The trouble is that we don't get interested in the commonplace things—and it is the commonplace things that go to make up the universe.

You have got to be a servant to somebody or something.

We have a lot of people revolutionizing the world because they never had to present a working model.

Do something different. My God, do something different!

We must use the past as a guidepost, not as a hitching post.

There will always be a frontier where there is an open mind and a willing hand.

The greatest thing this generation can do is to lay a few stepping-stones for the next generation.

It is man's destiny to ponder on the riddle of existence and, as a by-product of his wonderment, to create a new life on this earth.

IV

PUBLISHED SPEECHES, INTERVIEWS, AND ARTICLES OF CHARLES F. KETTERING

This partial list of publications is not a complete source of the sayings of Charles F. Kettering, as contained in this volume. Although references to most of his published speeches, interviews, and articles are given, much of the material in this volume has been taken from speeches which were not published.

"Some Points in Electric Lighting for Automobiles," *SAE Bulletin, 3,* 13, October, 1912.

"Self-Education," *Delco Doings,* (Dayton Engineering Laboratories Company), June 19, 1915.

"Engine Temperature Control," *SAE Bulletin, 10,* 685, September, 1916.

Address at SAE Chicago War Dinner, *SAE Journal,*[1] *2,* 118, February, 1918.

"Engineer's View of the Liberty Engine and the Airplane Program," *Scientific American,* June 8, 1918, page 538.

"Tractor Engineering Possibilities," *SAE Journal, 3,* 5, July, 1918.

Remarks, *SAE Journal, 3,* 14, July, 1918.

"The Future of the Airplane Business," *SAE Journal, 3,* 358, December, 1918.

"Automobile Power Plant," *Journal Western Society of Engineers, 24,* 31, January, 1919.

---

[1] From Volume 1 (1917) to Volume 21 (1927) the name of this publication was *The Journal of the Society of Automotive Engineers.*

Address at SAE Home-Coming Supper, *SAE Journal*, *4*, 258, April, 1919.

"More Efficient Utilization of Fuel," *SAE Journal*, *4*, 263, April, 1919.

Remarks, *SAE Journal*, *4*, 346, May, 1919.

Statement on the Fuel Problem, *SAE Journal*, *5*, 195, September, 1919.

Address at Tractor Demonstration Dinner, *SAE Journal*, *5*, 225, September, 1919.

"Studying the Knocks," *Scientific American*, October 11, 1919, page 364.

Address at Annual Banquet, Michigan Engineering Society, *The Michigan Engineer*, *37*, 79, 1919.

Remarks, *SAE Journal*, *6*, 332, May, 1920.

"Engineering Possibilities as Indicated by the Progress of Science," *SAE Journal*, *7*, 56, July, 1920.

"Combustion of Fuels in Internal Combustion Engines," *SAE Journal*, *7*, 224, September, 1920.

"Consumption—the Automotive Industry," *Amer. Petroleum Inst. Bulletin*, December 10, 1920, page 35. Also, in part, *SAE Journal*, *8*, 43, January, 1921.

Remarks at SAE Annual Dinner, *SAE Journal*, *8*, 250, March, 1921.

"The Spirit of Adventure in Education," *Bulletin No. 9*, Progressive Education Association, September, 1921.

"Fuel Research Developments," *SAE Journal*, *9*, 291, November, 1921.

"The Problems in Front of the Automotive Engineer," *SAE Journal*, *12*, 86, January, 1923.

Story of the Self-Starter, Dayton, Ohio, *Daily News,* May 20, 1923.

"Expect Great Things in the Automobile Industry," *Forbes Magazine,* October 13, 1923.

Address to American Petroleum Institute, *Amer. Petroleum Inst. Bulletin,* December 31, 1923, page 48.

"The Car You'll Drive 10 Years from Now," *Motor,* 84, January, 1924.

"Motor Design and Fuel Economy," *Industrial and Engineering Chemistry, 17,* 1115, November, 1925.

"The Engineer's Part in Increasing Highway Safety," *SAE Journal, 17,* 578, December, 1925.

"Research as Related to Banking," *The Cleveland Trust Monthly,* page 4, December, 1926.

"The Functions of Research," *Industrial and Engineering Chemistry, 10,* 1212, November, 1927.

"Research, Horse-Sense and Profits," *Factory and Industrial Management, 75,* 735, April, 1928.

"General Motors Budgets for Change," as told to Peter F. O'Shea, *The Magazine of Business, 54,* 359, October, 1928.

"The Engineer and His Opportunity," *SAE Journal, 23,* 350, October, 1928.

Commencement Address, *The Ohio State University Monthly,* July, 1929, page 452.

"Hurdles to Jump for Inventors," *Popular Mechanics,* December, 1929, page 954.

"Big Changes Ahead," as told to John T. Flynn, *The American Magazine,* January, 1930.

"Research Made Your Motor Car," *Scientific American,* January, 1930, page 9.

"Automotive Developments Held Back by Lack of True Anti-knock Fuels," *National Petroleum News, 22,* 27, April 30, 1930.

Address, Miami Valley Business Management Conference, *The Dayton Journal,* June 8, 1930.

"A Representation of the Dynamic Properties of Molecules by Mechanical Models," (with L. W. Shutts and D. H. Andrews), *Physical Review, 36,* 531, August 1, 1930.

"Fundamentals of Engineering Research," *Agricultural Engineering, 11,* 263, August, 1930.

"Research, Radio, Automobiles," *Electronics,* October, 1930, page 329.

"This Thing Called Research," *Executives Service Bulletin,* Metropolitan Life Insurance Company, *8,* 1, October, 1930.

"Unemployment and the Industrial System," as told to Lewis F. Carr, *The Saturday Evening Post,* December 13, 1930, page 16.

Address to Committee of 100 at Miami Beach, Florida, *Miami Daily News,* January 28, 1931, page 14.

"We Need New Things," as told to Ben Hibbs, *The Country Gentleman,* March, 1931, page 19.

"Business Needs a New Broom," *The Rotarian,* May, 1931, page 6.

"Coax Business Back," *Daily News Record,* June 18, 1931.

"Industry at the Crossroads," as told to Lewis F. Carr, *The Saturday Evening Post,* September 26, 1931, page 8.

"Electrical Synchronization of Marine Diesels," *Motorship,* March, 1932, page 114.

"The World Isn't Finished," as told to Lewis Carr, *The Saturday Evening Post,* April 25, 1932, page 23.

"The Role of Invention in Industry," *Journal of the Patent Office Society, 14,* 500, June, 1932.

"Some New Engineering Problems," *Industrial Record,* October, 1932, page 13.

The New Necessity, book, with Allen Orth, Century of Progress Series, Williams and Wilkins Company, 1932.

"Infrared Absorption Spectra of Certain Organic Compounds, Including the Principal Types Present in Gasoline" (with W.W. Sleator), *Physics, 4,* 39, February, 1933.

"Tomorrow We Move," as told to John T. Flynn, *The American Magazine,* March, 1933, page 24.

"Will the Goblins Get Us?" as told to Frazier Hunt, *Good Housekeeping,* April, 1933, page 43.

"America Comes Through a Crisis," as told to Paul de Kruif, *The Saturday Evening Post,* May 13, 1933, page 3.

"Relation of Chemistry to the Individual," *Industrial and Engineering Chemistry, 25,* 484, May, 1933.

"Ignorance Sires Argument," *SAE Journal, 33,* 13, November, 1933.

"Do We Need Birth Control of Ideas? No," as told to Malcolm W. Bingay, *The Rotarian,* April, 1934, page 8.

"Industry-Research," *Scientific American,* May, 1934, page 242.

Address, Annual Meeting, United States Chamber of Commerce, *Nation's Business,* June, 1934, page 22.

Contribution to Symposium, "Science and Industry in the Coming Century," *The Scientific Monthly,* July, 1934, page 68.

Address at Torch Club Dinner, *The Torch, 7,* 10, July, 1934.

"The Scientist in an Unscientific Society," *Scientific American,* August, 1934, page 79.

"It's Man's Turn Now," as told to Frazier Hunt, *Good Housekeeping,* January, 1935, page 16.

"The Motor Car of the Future," *Automobile Topics*, January 26, 1935, page 762.

"Looking Ahead with Boss Ket," as told to Frazier Hunt, *Popular Mechanics*, February, 1935, page 202.

"Industrial Prospecting," *Reprint and Circular Series No. 107*, National Research Council, December, 1935.

Address to New York State Bankers' Association, *Monthly Bulletin*, Robert Morris Associates, February, 1936, page 183.

"Research and Social Progress," *Journal Western Society of Engineers*, April, 1936, page 58. Also *Electrical Engineering*, April, 1936, page 324.

"How to Create a Labor Shortage," as told to Boyden Sparks, *The Saturday Evening Post*, May 30, 1936.

"Idea to Industry," *Journal of the Franklin Institute*, 222, 127, August, 1936.

"Looking Forward in Research, Science, and Industry," *Vital Speeches of the Day*, 3, 101, December 1, 1936.

"Research Makes Jobs," *Review of Reviews*, May, 1937, page 38.

"Research and Industry," *Scientific American*, May, 1937, page 285.

"Diesel Development," *G.M.A.C. News and Views*, November, 1937, page 24.

"Ten Paths to Fame and Fortune," as told to Beverly Smith, *American Magazine*, December, 1937.

"Engineering Principles of Diesel Design," *Official Proceedings, The Western Railway Club*, 50, 13, January, 1938.

"What Kettering Said," (at 1938 SAE Annual Meeting), *SAE Journal*, February, 1938, page 15.

"Joint Responsibility of Automotive and Civil Engineers," *American Society of Civil Engineers Proceedings, 64,* 1116, June, 1938.

"Scientific Training and Its Relation to Industrial Problems," *Journal of Applied Physics, 9,* 427, July, 1938.

"More Music, Please, Composers," as told to Neil M. Clark, *The Saturday Evening Post,* September 10, 1938, page 23.

"Research and Progress," *Armour Engineer and Alumnus,* December, 1938, page 6.

"We've Only Just Begun," *America's Future,* January, 1939, page 13.

"Industry's New Horizons," *Vital Speeches of the Day,* September 1, 1939, page 686.

"Transportation of Tomorrow," in book, *The Michigan-Life Conference on New Technologies in Transportation, Life* magazine, 1939.

"Effect of the Emergency on Scientific and Industrial Progress," *Vital Speeches of the Day,* December, 1939, page 93.

"Unfinished Business," *Industrial Medicine,* February, 1940, page 69.

"Looking Forward," extracts from address at banquet celebrating Sesqui-centennial of the United States Patent Law, *Ethyl News,* April, 1940.

"Opportunities for Youth," *Vital Speeches of the Day,* June 1, 1940, page 504.

"The Age of Opportunity," *Popular Mechanics,* October, 1940.

"Guns Aren't Windshield Wipers," as told to J. C. Furnas, *The Saturday Evening Post,* January 18, 1941, page 12.

"Application of Modern Science to the Plating Industry," *Monthly Review of the American Electroplaters' Society,* January, 1941, page 15.

"The World Ahead," *Printers' Ink Monthly,* February, 1941, page 12.

"The Future Is Anything You Want It To Be," *Think,* August, 1941, page 30.

"New Vistas for Mankind After the War," *Liberty,* February 21, 1942, page 10.

"There Is Only One Mistake: To Do Nothing," *The Saturday Evening Post,* March 28, 1942.

"Horsepower Is War Power," *Scientific American,* July, 1942, page 4.

"We Are Learning To Do the Impossible," *GM Folks,* October, 1942.

Address, Union League Club of Chicago, *Union League Bulletin,* December, 1942, page 6.

"Inventors Don't Invent Enough," as told to Malcolm W. Bingay, Booklet, *A World to Live In,* Rotary International, 1942.

"The Role of Patents in the Automobile Industry's Growth," *Journal of Commerce,* Special Section, March 11, 1943, page 11.

"Chemistry and the Motor Car Industry," *Chemical and Engineering News, 21,* 841, June 10, 1943.

"Looking Forward," *Vital Speeches of the Day,* June, 1943, page 532.

"Looking at the Future Through the Eyes of Research," *SAE Journal, 51,* 33, July, 1943

"How to Plan for Victory," as told to Beverly Smith, *American Magazine,* December, 1943, page 19.

"Education Begins at Home," *School and Society,* January 1, 1944, page 10. Abridged in *Reader's Digest,* February, 1944, page 80.

"How Can We Develop Inventors?" *Mechanical Engineering, 66,* 231, April, 1944.

Address, Ordnance Engineering Round Table Conference, *Army Ordnance,* May–June, 1944.

"Catching Up with Nature," *Vital Speeches of the Day,* September 15, 1944, page 736.

"Inertia of the Carrier of Electricity in Copper and Aluminum" (with G. G. Scott), *Physical Review, 66,* 257 and 267, November 1 and 15, 1944.

"The Effect of the Molecular Structure of Fuels on the Power and Efficiency of Internal Combustion Engines," *Industrial and Engineering Chemistry, 36,* 1079, December, 1944.

"Research Opens the Door," *Scientific American,* January, 1945, page 7.

"Some Secrets of the Postwar Period," *Executives' Club News* (Executives' Club of Chicago), *21,* 3, March 23, 1945.

"Relationship of Research to Management," *Manufacturers' News,* April, 1945, page 9.

"Fuels and Engines for Higher Power and Greater Efficiency," *SAE Journal (Transactions), 53,* 352, June, 1945.

"Within Yourself," *Boys' Life,* August, 1945, page 3.

Address to American Society for Testing Materials, *ASTM Bulletin,* December, 1945, page 15.

Commencement Address, Syracuse University, Syracuse University Brochure, Seventy-fifth Anniversary celebration, 1945, page 44.

Discussion, page 67 of book, *The Future of Industrial Research,* Standard Oil Development Company, 1945.

"The Farm—A Mode of Life," Address at 24th Annual 4-H Club Congress, *News and Views, GMAC, GEIC, MIC,* January, 1946, page 7.

"Get Out of That Rut!" *The Rotarian,* February, 1946, page 8.

"War Sidetracks Science," *Nation's Business,* April, 1946, page 37.

"Muscles and Machines," *Vital Speeches of the Day,* July 1, 1946, page 575.

"Medicine and Industrial Research," *Journal Michigan State Medical Society,* August, 1946, page 1063.

Address, Western Railway Club Meeting, *Official Proceedings, Western Railway Club,* November, 1946, page 12.

"The Future of Science," *Science, 104,* 609, December 27, 1946.

"What Is Our Competition?" *Diesel Power and Diesel Transportation,* January, 1947, page 92.

"Thomas Alva Edison," *The Scientific Monthly, 64,* 109, February, 1947.

Address, The Inland Daily Press Association, *Members Service Bulletin,* June 26, 1947, page 235.

"Chemistry and the Automobile Industry," *Record of Chemical Progress, 8,* 58, July–October, 1947.

"More Efficient Utilization of Fuels," *SAE Quarterly Transactions, 1,* 669, October, 1947

"American Battle for Abundance, A Story of Mass Production" (with Allen Orth), booklet, General Motors Corporation, 1947.

"Biographical Memoir of Leo Hendrik Baekeland," Eighth Memoir, Volume XXIV, National Academy of Sciences, 1947.

"Biographical Memoir of Thomas Midgley, Jr.," Eleventh Memoir, Volume XXIV, National Academy of Sciences, 1947.

"Take Ethyl, for Example," *Ethyl News,* February, 1948, page 7.

Address, Second Joint Industry-Faculty Conference on Engineering Management, April 27, 1948, *Engineering Experiment Station Bulletin Series No. 12,* Louisiana State University.

Address on Receipt of Third Annual API Gold Medal, *Proceedings 28th Annual Meeting*, American Petroleum Institute, *28*, 26, 1948.

"Technical Education," *Air Affairs*, Winter, 1948, page 223.

"Age of Mechanical Power from Liquid Fuel," *Oil Forum*, November, 1949, page 479.

"Get Off Route 25, Young Man," as told to Vice-Admiral Harold G. Bowen, USN (Ret.), *Collier's*, December 3, 1949, page 13.

"Future Developments in Transportation," *Journal of the Franklin Institute, 251,* 109, January, 1951.

"Education as the Guardian of the American Heritage," *Vital Speeches of the Day*, March 15, 1951, page 346.

"Science and Technology—Servants of Man," Addresses and Proceedings of the Seventy-Fifth Anniversary, 1948–1949, The Ohio State University, 1951, page 44.

"And Then Came the Horseless Carriage," *Popular Mechanics*, January, 1952, page 137.

"Don't Be Afraid to Stumble," *The Rotarian*, January, 1952, page 8.

"An Engineer's Report on the Future," *American Engineer*, October, 1952.

Dedication Address, Lobund Institute, in "Science and Society" brochure, University of Notre Dame, 1952.

"A Review of the Century," Centennial of Engineering, History and Proceedings of Symposia, Museum of Science and Industry, Chicago, 1953, page 46.

"The Engineers' Responsibility in Educating the Public," *Mechanical Engineering, 75,* 953, December, 1953.

"Satisfied?—Watch Out!" *ISA Journal*, January, 1955, page 1.

"You Haven't Seen Anything Yet," *The Foundation,* Engineering Society of Detroit, June, 1955.

"An Inventor Looks at Education," *Proceedings of the Sixth Thomas Alva Edison Foundation Institute,* 1955, New York University Press, page 52.

"A Tribute to Automobile Old Timers," *Old Timers News,* Winter, 1955, page 17.

"I Am Interested in the Future," *Sales Management,* March 1, 1956, page 88.

"The Inventor Looks at Education," brochure *Conference of Maryland High School Principals,* April 12 and 13, 1956, Maryland State Department of Education.

"Start Now to Make America's Progress Your Profession" (advertisement sponsored by the American Petroleum Institute), *The Saturday Evening Post,* October 20, 1956, page 88 (also in other periodicals).

Address, Cleveland Chamber of Commerce Luncheon, *Cleveland Engineering,* August 22, 1957, page 10.

Foreword to brochure, "Cooperative Education and the Impending Educational Crises," Thomas Alva Edison Foundation, 1957.

"Future Unlimited," *The Saturday Evening Post,* May 17, 1958, page 126.

"Engineering," *Journal American Medical Association, 167,* 1360, July 12, 1958.

Address and remarks in brochure, "In Memoriam, Charles F. Kettering," Southern Research Institute, Birmingham, Alabama, 1959, pages 15, 34, 48, 53, 61, 65, 70, 75, 82, 88, and 92.

"Short Stories of Science and Invention, a Collection of Radio Talks," given in connection with General Motors Symphony of the Air, September, 1942, to July, 1945. Public Relations Staff, General Motors Corporation, 1959.